D1177524

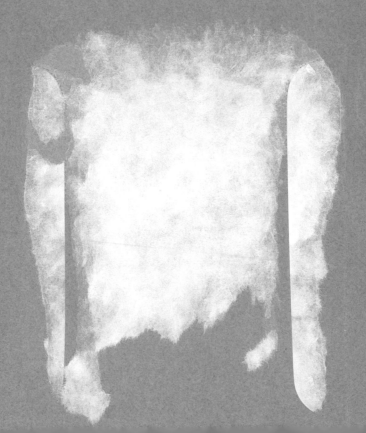

The Giant Book

THE
GIANT BOOK

Beatrice Schenk de Regniers

DRAWINGS BY WILLIAM LAHEY CUMMINGS

ATHENEUM   *1966*   NEW YORK

To Francis, a giant in the best sense of the word

Contents

Contents

III BIG GIANTS AND TALL TALES

Introduction

Maybe somewhere there was a place—maybe sometime there was a time—when people did not have stories about giants. But I have never heard of such a place or such a time.

The Bible tells of giants. Old, old legends and myths tell of great battles between giants and gods. People today make up stories about giants.

In fact, there are so many giants and so many stories about them, that the most gigantic book I can think of could not hold all the stories about all the giants.

But just what is *giant size?*

An elephant the size of an elephant is not a giant. But if a flea were the size of an elephant, we would call it a giant flea. And compared to an ant, you are a giant. It seems we consider a thing giant size in comparison with its normal size or in comparison with something or someone else.

vii

The smallest giant in this book, Goliath, is about nine and one half feet tall. But Goliath would look like a peanut next to the giant Og who, according to Jewish legend, was so big that an ivory bed large enough to hold two people could be carved out of one of his teeth.

The giant Cormoran in *Jack the Giant-killer* is eighteen feet tall. That is about average height for fairy-tale giants. And it is a good size for a giant, I think. An eighteen-foot giant is big enough to be good and scary, and yet it is easy to imagine just how tall he is. All you have to do is to remember that eighteen feet is as tall as three tall men standing one on top of the other. It is harder to imagine a giant several miles high. And that is probably why fairy-tale giants are more frightening than the bigger giants we read about in myths—Atlas, for example, who supports the sky.

Although fairy tale giants are the scariest, they are also the most stupid. It seems that any reasonably bright lad who also has a good deal of courage can fool a giant, even a giant with three heads!

It does bother me a bit that the heroes in many of these stories are so tricky and deceitful. But that's how they were, so that's how you'll find them in this collection. And I suppose that without quick wit and cunning

—and often a bit of magic, too—it would be hard for a boy to overcome a man-eating giant eighteen feet high. Still, I must confess there are times when my sympathy goes out to those befuddled, bedeviled, and bamboozled giants—ogres though they may be.

But don't make the mistake of thinking that all giants are stupid. There are giants that outwit gods, and you will find in this book a story of a giant who, with the help of his clever giantess wife, outwits another giant.

There are giants, too, who are great heroes.

In America, for example, we rather like whatever is big just because it *is* big. We boast of giant skyscrapers and giant bridges and giant highways. We often choose the giant economy size whether we buy soap flakes or candy bars. And when we want to say a man is a great man, we call him a giant. We speak of giants of science or of literature, for example.

So it is only natural that when men in the lumber camps of North America—in Canada or in Maine or in Minnesota—began making up stories about a lumberjack hero, Paul Bunyan, he turned out to be a giant. But this giant was as intelligent and kind as he was big and powerful.

Each man who told about Paul Bunyan tried to tell a taller tale than the next man, and so the stories grew, each story more preposterous and funnier than the one before. Much later, people put these tall tales in writing so we would have them always. In this collection you can read some Paul Bunyan stories taken from the very best book I could find. If you want more, you can read the book they came from. (And if you want to know what Paul Bunyan looked like—or what someone thought he looked like—you can go to Bimidji, Minnesota, where they have a gigantic wooden statue of Paul Bunyan dressed in his lumberjack clothes.)

When the old stories about giants were first told, before they were ever put into books, they were told for a grown-up audience. (But I'm sure children managed to hear them too. Children have always known ways to make themselves invisible when they want to stay around and listen to grown-up talk.)

Anyhow, it was big rough lumberjacks who first heard of Paul Bunyan's exploits. And it was kings and queens and their guests who heard the poet Homer recite the tale of Odysseus and his adventures (including his encounter with the giant, Polyphemus, that you will read about on page 70).

The old myths and legends about battles between gods and giants were told or sung to men and women, and believed by them. It was through myth and legend that the ancients transmitted religion and history—and their science, too. (They didn't know the real cause of earthquakes, so it made sense to believe that earthquakes were caused by an angry giant stamping his foot.)

The fairy tales, too, which came much later than the myths and legends, were told mostly by men to other men. Soldiers whiling away the evening in their barracks used to tell them. Farmers and fishermen and other countryfolk, when they met together after their work, would listen to some of the very stories you will find in this book.

And even when some of the fairy tales were first put into writing, they were meant to be read by gentlemen and ladies of the king's court. I am thinking especially of the court of King Louis XIV of France and of a man named Charles Perrault who wrote "Little Red Riding Hood," "Sleeping Beauty," "Cinderella," and others you know so well.

There is one story in this book that does not come

from myth or legend or folklore. It is the story of Gulliver's adventures in the country of the giants, and it was written by Jonathan Swift who lived about two hundred and fifty years ago. When Swift wrote, he had no idea that his book would appeal to young readers.

But children know a good thing when they see it, and so, gradually, they have inherited the priceless treasure of giant stories. Now it is grown-ups who sneak in to listen to or read these tales.

As each of the stories in this book is presented to you, you may somehow get the idea that I believe there really are giants. Well, the truth is, when I'm reading about giants or when I'm writing about giants, I really believe there are giants. And I advise you to do the same. That is the best way to enjoy this book.

BEATRICE SCHENK DE REGNIERS
NEW YORK (THAT GIGANTIC CITY!)

Killer Giants and Giant-killers

Jack the Giant-killer
History of the Giants
Jack and the Beanstalk
The Nine-headed Giant
David and Goliath

Jack the Giant-killer

Here are six famous adventures of the most adventurous giant-killer of all time.

In the time of King Arthur, there lived near the Land's End of England, in the County of Cornwall, a worthy farmer who had an only son named Jack.

Jack took pleasure in hearing or reading stories of wizards, conjurers, and giants. And he used to listen eagerly when his father talked of the brave knights of King Arthur's Round Table.

Jack himself was a boy of bold temper and lively wit, and he could outrun, outwrestle, and outwit any boy or man in the County of Cornwall.

3

The First Adventure

In those days there lived on St. Michael's Mount off the coast of Cornwall a fierce and monstrous giant, eighteen feet high and about three yards around the middle. His name was Cormoran, and he was the terror of all the neighboring towns and villages.

It was his custom to come down from the mount and wade over to the mainland every evening and seize upon all the cattle he could find. He thought nothing of carrying half a dozen oxen on his back at one time. And as for sheep and hogs, he would tie them by the dozen around his waist so that they hung about him like a bunch of candles.

Jack resolved to kill this monster. So he took a horn, a shovel, and a pickaxe. And early in a dark winter evening he swam over to the Mount. There he fell to work at once, and before morning he had dug a pit twenty-two feet deep and almost as many broad. Jack covered it at the top with sticks and straw, and strewed earth over it to make it look like solid ground.

He then blew on his horn such a loud and long tantivy, that the giant awoke and came towards Jack roaring like thunder.

4

"You saucy villain, you shall pay dearly for breaking my rest! I will broil you for my breakfast!"

The giant had hardly spoken these words when, coming one step further, he tumbled headlong into the pit. His fall shook the very mountain. The giant tried to rise, but Jack struck him a blow on the crown of his head with the pickaxe, which killed him at once.

Jack hastened back to rejoice his friends with the news of the giant's death.

The Justices of Cornwall declared Jack should always be called

JACK THE GIANT-KILLER.

And they gave him a sword and a belt upon which was embroidered in letters of gold:

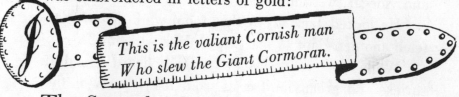

*This is the valiant Cornish man
Who slew the Giant Cormoran.*

The Second Adventure

Another giant called Blunderbore swore to have revenge on Jack. He kept an enchanted castle in the midst of a lonely wood.

One day Jack passed through this wood and, sitting down to rest near a pleasant fountain, he fell asleep.

When the giant Blunderbore came to the fountain for water, he found Jack there. Blunderbore read the golden words on Jack's belt. Then he quietly lifted Jack onto his shoulders to carry him to his castle.

As they passed through a thicket, the rustling of the leaves awoke Jack. He was sadly afraid when he found himself in the clutches of Blunderbore.

Yet this was nothing to his fright soon after. For when they reached the castle the giant took Jack into a large room, where lay the hearts and livers of persons who had been lately killed. And Blunderbore told Jack with a horrid grin that men's hearts, eaten with pepper and vinegar, were his nicest food.

He locked Jack up in that room while he went to fetch another giant to feast upon Jack with him.

While the giant was away, Jack heard dreadful shrieks and groans and cries from many parts of the castle. And soon after, he heard a mournful voice repeat these lines:

"Haste, valiant stranger, haste away,
    Lest you become the giant's prey.

On his return he'll bring another
Still more savage than his brother—

"A horrid cruel monster who,
Before he kills will torture you.
Oh valiant stranger! Haste away,
Or you'll become the giant's prey."

Jack looked out of the window and saw the giants coming arm in arm. "Now," said Jack to himself, "either my death or freedom is at hand."

There were two strong ropes in the room. Jack made a large noose with a slipknot at the end of each rope. He fastened the other ends to a beam at the ceiling. Then, as the giants passed under the window, Jack threw the ropes over their heads and pulled with all his might till he had strangled them.

Jack slid down the ropes, took a bunch of keys from Blunderbore's pocket, and went in to search the castle. There he found three ladies tied up by the hair of their heads and almost starved to death.

"Ladies," said Jack, "I have put an end to the monster and his wicked brother, and I give you this castle and all the riches it contains."

The Third Adventure

Jack went further on his journey, and met King Arthur's only son, who was traveling into Wales to deliver a beautiful lady from the power of a magician. Jack saw that the prince had no servants with him and begged leave to attend him.

When night came on, the prince, who had just given his last penny to an old woman, asked Jack, "How are we to get food for ourselves? And where are we to sleep this night?"

"Leave that to me, sir," said Jack. "And be of good heart. Two miles further there lives a giant whom I know well. He has three heads and will fight five hundred men. My lord, leave me to manage him and wait here till I return."

Jack rode on to the gates of the castle and gave a loud knock. The giant, with a voice like thunder, roared out, "Who is there?"

Jack said, "No one but your poor cousin Jack."

"Well," said the giant, "what news, cousin Jack?"

"Dear cousin," said Jack, "I have heavy news."

"Pooh!" said the giant. "What heavy news can come

8

to me—a giant who can fight five hundred men?"

"Alas," said Jack, "here is King Arthur's son coming with two thousand men to kill you."

"Oh, cousin Jack, this is heavy news indeed! But I have a large cellar underground, where I will hide myself, and you shall lock, bolt, and bar me in, and keep the keys till the King's son is gone."

When Jack had locked the giant in, he went back and fetched the prince, and they feasted and made themselves merry, then slept soundly in the giant's own bed.

In the morning, after sending the prince on ahead, Jack released the giant.

"Oh, cousin Jack," cried the giant, "what can I give you as a reward for saving my life?"

"I desire nothing," said Jack, "but the old coat and cap, with the old rusty sword and slippers that are hanging near your bed."

"You shall have them," said the giant, "for they are things of great use: the coat will keep you invisible; the cap will give you knowledge; the sword will cut through anything; and the shoes are of extraordinary swiftness."

Jack thanked the giant and went on his way.

He quickly caught up with the prince, and soon they

came to the dwelling of the beautiful lady who was under the power of a wicked magician. The lady received the prince politely and ordered a fine dinner to be prepared.

When the dinner was ended, the lady rose, wiped her mouth with a handkerchief, and said, "My lord, you must show me this handkerchief tomorrow morning or lose your head." With that she smiled cruelly and left the room, taking the handkerchief with her.

The prince went to bed with a heavy heart. But Jack put on his Cap of Knowledge, which told him that the lady was forced by the power of enchantment to meet the wicked magician every night in the middle of the forest.

Jack put on his Coat of Darkness, which made him invisible, and his Shoes of Swiftness, and reached the forest just in time to see her give the handkerchief to the magician. With one blow of his Sword of Sharpness, Jack cut off the magician's head.

At that very moment the enchantment was ended and the lady was restored to her virtue and goodness. She was married to the prince on the next day, and all three returned to the court of King Arthur.

There Jack, for his great deeds, was made a Knight of the Round Table.

The Fourth Adventure

Jack resolved not to be idle for the future. So he left the Court, taking with him his Cap of Knowledge, his Sword of Sharpness, his Shoes of Swiftness, and his Coat of Darkness.

He came to a large forest, and had hardly entered when he heard dreadful shrieks. A monstrous giant was dragging along by their hair a handsome knight and his beautiful lady.

Jack put on his Coat of Darkness, under which he carried his Sword of Sharpness, and ran at the giant. But this giant was so tall, Jack could not even reach as high as the giant's knees. So, with one stroke of his Sword of Sharpness, Jack cut through the giant's legs. When the huge body toppled to the ground, the trees shook and the earth itself trembled. Then with another stroke of his sword, Jack cut off the giant's head.

The knight and his lady thanked Jack heartily and invited him to their castle.

"No," said Jack. "I cannot be at ease till I find out the giant's den."

"Noble stranger," replied the knight, "this monster

lives in a cave under yonder mountain with a brother giant more cruel than himself. Do not risk your life a second time, but come with us instead."

"No," answered Jack. "If there be twenty giants, not one shall escape my fury."

The Fifth Adventure

Jack got on his horse, and had not gone a mile before he saw the giant's brother, sitting on a huge rock in front of a cave.

The giant had a great iron club by his side, but he could not see Jack, who was wearing his Coat of Darkness. So Jack came quite close to the giant and struck a blow at his head with the Sword of Sharpness. But he missed his aim, and cut off the giant's nose instead of his head. The giant roared and howled and beat the air with his iron club. Jack, however, slipped nimbly behind the giant, jumped up on the rock, and drove the sword through the giant's body. Then he cut off the giant's head and sent it, with the head of the brother, to King Arthur.

Now Jack went into the cave where he found rooms full of gold and jewels.

12

He wandered further through many passageways until he came to the giants' great dining room. A huge pot filled with boiling water stood at one end of the room. At the other end was a kind of pantry filled with miserable captives. The giant kept these unfortunate men and women behind bars until he was ready to boil them for his dinner.

Jack set the captives free.

"I make you a gift of the giants' treasure," he told them. And he bade them good-by and set out in search of new adventures.

The Sixth Adventure

At the foot of a high mountain, he knocked at the door of a very small house and an old man let him in.

"Good father," said Jack, "can you lodge a traveler?"

"Yes," said the hermit, "I can, if you will accept such fare as my house affords."

Jack entered, and the old man set before him some bread and meat. When Jack had eaten, the hermit said, "My son, I know you are the famous conqueror of giants. On the top of this mountain is an enchanted castle kept

13

by a giant named Galligantus and his companion, an evil wizard. Galligantus gets many knights into his castle, where the wizard turns them into the shapes of beasts.

"Above all, I lament the hard fate of a duke's daughter whom they have captured and turned into the shape of a deer. Many knights have tried to rescue her, yet no one has been able to get past the two fiery griffins that guard the gate of the castle."

Jack put on his Coat of Darkness, passed the fiery griffins, and reached the castle gate. A golden trumpet was hanging there, and underneath was written:

Whoever can this trumpet blow
Shall cause the giant's overthrow.

Jack blew a shrill blast on the trumpet, which made the castle vanish like smoke. When the giant Galligantus stooped to pick up his club, Jack cut off his head. The wizard was carried away by a whirlwind, and at that moment, the duke's daughter returned to her proper form. And all the knights who had been changed into beasts became knights again.

Jack sent the giant's head to be added to King Arthur's collection. Soon after, Jack followed with the duke's daughter and the knights he had rescued.

14

By this time, Jack's fame had spread through the whole country.

At the king's request, the duke gave Jack his daughter in marriage, to the joy of all the kingdom. And the king gave Jack a large estate on which Jack and his lady lived the rest of their days in joy and content, beloved and respected by all.

The History of the Giants

These fierce giants come from a book over a hundred years old. The book is called *The History of the Giants*, and it is 2½ inches tall and 2⅛ inches wide —just like the pages you see here.

You could make your own little giant book—draw your own pictures and write your own verses. Maybe you would like to begin by drawing the giants to go with these verses:

Giant Glum lives in a cave.
He eats all boys who misbehave.

Giant Gloom lived in the city.
He ate all the people—what a pity.

Giant Gruff would rant and rave
Because he did not like to shave.

Giant Glub lived in a well
Into which many people fell.

You should be able to make up verses as good as or better than these!

OLD GIANT MUMBO.

Old Mumbo living in a wood,
Eat all the boys and girls he could.

THE IRISH GIANT.

The Irish Giant, Ben the Big,
On a lofty mountain liv'd,
He was of all the land he wonder,
And when he spoke he roar'd like
thunder.

A B C D E F G H I

J K L M N O P Q R

S T U V W X Y Z

......

1 2 3 4 5 6 7 8 9 0

Giant Grim liv'd in Thrace,
He scar'd the boys with his face,
He was as big as a church,
And as tall as a steeple.
And when he appear'd
He frighten'd the people.

Jack and the Beanstalk

Now here's another lad named Jack, sharp as a needle and bold as brass. And here's another English giant—the kind that likes to eat boys broiled on toast.

There was once upon a time a poor widow who had an only son named Jack, and a cow named Milky-white. And all they had to live on was the milk the cow gave every morning, which they carried to the market and sold. But one morning Milky-white gave no milk, and they didn't know what to do.

"What shall we do, what shall we do?" said the widow, wringing her hands.

"Cheer up, Mother, I'll go and get work somewhere," said Jack.

"We've tried that before, and nobody would take you," said his mother; "we must sell Milky-white and with the money start shop, or something."

18

"All right, Mother," says Jack; "it's market-day today, and I'll soon sell Milky-white, and then we'll see what we can do."

So he took the cow's halter in his hand, and off he started. He hadn't gone far when he met a funny looking old man, who said to him: "Good morning, Jack."

"Good morning to you," said Jack, and wondered how he knew his name.

"Well, Jack, and where are you off to?" said the man.

"I'm going to market to sell our cow here."

"Oh, you look the proper sort of chap to sell cows," said the man; "I wonder if you know how many beans make five."

"Two in each hand and one in your mouth," says Jack, as sharp as a needle.

"Right you are," says the man, "and here they are, the very beans themselves," he went on, pulling out of his pocket a number of strange-looking beans. "As you are so sharp," says he, "I don't mind doing a swop with you—your cow for these beans."

"Go along," says Jack; "wouldn't you like it?"

"Ah! you don't know what these beans are," said the man; "if you plant them overnight, by morning

19

they grow right up to the sky."

"Really?" said Jack; "you don't say so."

"Yes, that is so, and if it doesn't turn out to be true you can have your cow back."

"Right," says Jack, and hands him over Milky-white's halter and pockets the beans.

Back goes Jack home, and as he hadn't gone very far it wasn't dusk by the time he got to his door.

"Back already, Jack?" said his mother; "I see you haven't got Milky-white, so you've sold her. How much did you get for her?"

"You'll never guess, mother," says Jack.

"No, you don't say so. Good boy! Five pounds, ten, fifteen, no, it can't be twenty."

"I told you you couldn't guess. What do you say to these beans; they're magical, plant them overnight and——"

"What!" says Jack's mother, "have you been such a fool, such a dolt, such an idiot, as to give away my Milky-white, the best milker in the parish, and prime beef to boot, for a set of paltry beans? Take that! Take that! Take that! And as for your precious beans here they go out of the window. And now off with you to bed. Not a sup shall you drink, and not a bite shall you

20

swallow this very night."

So Jack went upstairs to his little room in the attic, and sad and sorry he was, to be sure, as much for his mother's sake, as for the loss of his supper.

At last he dropped off to sleep.

When he woke up, the room looked so strange. The sun was shining into part of it, and yet all the rest was quite dark and shady. So Jack jumped up and dressed himself and went to the window. And what do you think he saw? Why, the beans his mother had thrown out of the window into the garden had sprung up into a big beanstalk which went up and up and up till it reached the sky. So the man spoke truth after all.

The beanstalk grew up quite close past Jack's window, so all he had to do was to open it and give a jump on to the beanstalk, which ran up just like a big ladder. So Jack climbed, and he climbed and he climbed and he climbed and he climbed and he climbed and he climbed till at last he reached the sky. And when he got there he found a long broad road going as straight as a dart. So he walked along and he walked along and he walked along till he came to a great big tall house, and on the doorstep there was a great big tall woman.

"Good morning, mum," says Jack, quite polite-like.

"Could you be so kind as to give me some breakfast?" For he hadn't had anything to eat you know, the night before, and was as hungry as a hunter.

"It's breakfast you want, is it?" says the great big tall woman. "It's breakfast you'll be if you don't move off from here. My man is a giant and there's nothing he likes better than boys broiled on toast. You'd better be moving on or he'll soon be coming."

"Oh! please mum, do give me something to eat, mum. I've had nothing to eat since yesterday morning, really and truly, mum," says Jack. "I may as well be broiled as die of hunger."

Well, the giant's wife was not half so bad after all. So she took Jack into the kitchen, and gave him a chunk of bread and cheese and a jug of milk. But Jack hadn't half finished these when thump! thump! thump! the whole house began to tremble with the noise of someone coming.

"Goodness gracious me! It's my old man," said the giant's wife, "what on earth shall I do? Come along quick and jump in here." And she bundled Jack into the oven just as the giant came in.

He was a big one, to be sure. At his belt he had three calves strung up by the heels, and he unhooked them

and threw them down on the table and said, "Here
wife, broil me a couple of these for breakfast. Ah!
what's this I smell?

"Fee-fi-fo-fum,
 I smell the blood of an Englishman,
 Be he alive, or be he dead
 I'll grind his bones to make my bread."

"Nonsense, dear," said his wife, "you're dreaming.
Or perhaps you smell the scraps of that little boy you
liked so much for yesterday's dinner. Here, you go and
have a wash and tidy up, and by the time you come back
your breakfast'll be ready for you."

So off the giant went, and Jack was just going to
jump out of the oven and run away when the woman
told him not. "Wait till he's asleep," says she; "he always has a doze after breakfast."

Well, the giant had his breakfast, and after that he
goes to a big chest and takes out of it a couple of bags of
gold, and down he sits and counts till at last his head
began to nod and he began to snore till the whole house
shook again.

Then Jack crept out on tiptoe from his oven. And as

he was passing the giant he took one of the bags of gold under his arm, and off he pelters till he came to the beanstalk, and then he threw down the bag of gold, which of course fell into his mother's garden, and then he climbed down and climbed down till at last he got home and told his mother and showed her the gold and said: "Well, mother, wasn't I right about the beans? They are really magical, you see."

So they lived on the bag of gold for some time, but at last they came to the end of it, and Jack made up his mind to try his luck once more up at the top of the beanstalk. So one fine morning he rose up early, and got on to the beanstalk, and he climbed and he climbed and he climbed and he climbed and he climbed and he climbed till at last he came out on to the road again and up to the great big tall house he had been to before. There, sure enough, was the great big tall woman a-standing on the doorstep.

"Good morning, mum," says Jack, as bold as brass, "could you be so good as to give me something to eat?"

"Go away my boy," said the big tall woman, "or else my man will eat you up for breakfast. But aren't you the youngster who came here once before? Do you know, that very day, my man missed one of his bags of gold."

25

"That's strange, mum," said Jack, "I dare say I could tell you something about that, but I'm so hungry I can't speak till I've had something to eat."

Well the big tall woman was so curious that she took him in and gave him something to eat. But he had scarcely begun munching it as slowly as he could when thump! thump! thump! they heard the giant's footsteps, and the giant's wife hid Jack away in the oven.

All happened as it did before. In came the giant as he did before, said: "Fee-fi-fo-fum," and had his breakfast off three broiled oxen. Then he said, "Wife, bring me the hen that lays the golden eggs." So she brought it, and the giant said, "Lay," and it laid an egg all of gold. And then the giant began to nod his head, and to snore till the house shook.

Then Jack crept out of the oven on tiptoe and caught hold of the golden hen, and was off before you could say "Jack Robinson." But this time the hen gave a cackle which woke the giant, and just as Jack got out of the house he heard him calling, "Wife, wife, what have you done with my golden hen?"

And the wife said: "Why, my dear?"

But that was all Jack heard, for he rushed off to the beanstalk and climbed down like a house on fire. And when he got home he showed his mother the wonderful hen, and said "Lay" to it; and it laid a golden egg every time he said "Lay."

Well, Jack was not content, and it wasn't very long before he determined to have another try at his luck up there at the top of the beanstalk. So one fine morning, he rose up early, and got on to the beanstalk, and he climbed and he climbed and he climbed and he climbed till he got to the top. But this time he knew better than to go straight to the giant's house. And when he got near it, he waited behind a bush till he saw the giant's wife come out with a pail to get some water, and then he crept into the house and got into the copper kettle. He hadn't been there long when he heard thump! thump! thump! as before, and in came the giant and his wife.

"Fee-fi-fo-fum, I smell the blood of an Englishman," cried out the giant. "I smell him, wife, I smell him."

"Do you, my dearie?" says the giant's wife. "Then, if it's that little rogue that stole your gold and the hen that laid the golden eggs he's sure to have got into the oven." And they both rushed to the oven. But Jack wasn't there, luckily, and the giant's wife said: "There you are again with your fee-fi-fo-fum. Why of course it's the boy you caught last night that I've just broiled for

27

your breakfast. How forgetful I am, and how careless you are not to know the difference between live and dead after all these years."

So the giant sat down to the breakfast and ate it, but every now and then he would mutter: "Well, I could have sworn——" and he'd get up and search the larder and the cupboards and everything, only, luckily, he didn't think of the kettle.

After breakfast was over, the giant called out, "Wife, wife, bring me my golden harp." So she brought it and put it on the table before him. Then he said: "Sing!" and the golden harp sang most beautifully. And it went on singing till the giant fell asleep, and commenced to snore like thunder.

Then Jack lifted up the kettle lid very quietly and got down like a mouse and crept on hands and knees till he came to the table when up he crawled, caught hold of the golden harp and dashed with it towards the door. But the harp called out quite loud: "Master! Master!" and the giant woke up just in time to see Jack running off with his harp.

Jack ran as fast as he could, and the giant came rushing after, and would soon have caught him only Jack had a start and dodged him a bit and knew where he was

28

going. When he got to the beanstalk the giant was not more than twenty yards away when suddenly he saw Jack disappear like, and when he came to the end of the road he saw Jack underneath climbing down for dear life. Well, the giant didn't like trusting himself to such a ladder, and he stood and waited. So Jack got another start. But just then the harp cried out: "Master! Master!" and the giant swung himself down on to the beanstalk, which shook with his weight. Down climbs Jack, and after him climbed the giant. By this time Jack had climbed down and climbed down and climbed down till he was very nearly home. So he called out: "Mother! Mother! Bring me an axe, bring me an axe." And his mother came rushing out with the axe in her hand, but when she came to the beanstalk she stood stock still with fright for there she saw the giant with his legs just through the clouds.

But Jack jumped down and got hold of the axe and gave a chop at the beanstalk which cut it half in two. The giant felt the beanstalk shake and quiver so he stopped to see what was the matter. Then Jack gave another chop with the axe and the beanstalk was cut in two and began to topple over. The giant fell down and broke his crown, and the beanstalk came toppling after.

Then Jack showed his mother his golden harp, and what with showing that and selling the golden eggs Jack and his mother became very rich, and Jack married a great princess, and they lived happy ever after.

PEOPLE WHO BELIEVED IN GIANTS USED TO SAY—

A CAVE—is the hollow bone of a giant's leg.

The Nine-headed Giant

At the very time you are reading about this horrible monster some children and grownups in Korea may be listening to this same shivery story—for Korea is where this story comes from.

There was once a giant with nine heads who lived in a cave high up in the mountains. From time to time he would come down to the nearest village and carry off one or two people.

All the villagers lived in terror of the giant and were constantly trying to think up some scheme to overcome him.

One day a beautiful woman and her maidservant went to the well to draw water and were carried off by the giant.

When the news was brought to the woman's husband, he set off at once to rescue his wife. But before he could rescue her he must find her, and no one in the village knew just where the giant lived.

31

So the man went over a hill and into the next valley where he came to a thatched cottage in the woods.

An old woman sat in the doorway pounding rice.

"Can you tell me where the nine-headed giant lives?" asked the man. "He has carried off my wife and her maidservant and I am on my way to rescue them."

No, the old woman could not tell him where the giant lived. But she told him to go over the hill and into the next valley and he would come to a woman washing radishes.

So he went over the hill and into the next valley and there he found an old woman washing radishes.

"Good day, old woman," said the man. "Can you tell me where the nine-headed giant lives? He has carried off my beautiful wife and her maidservant, and I must rescue them."

Thereupon the old woman gave him a radish and said, "That giant is exceedingly strong. So eat this radish; then go and lift the heavy stone over there."

It was not really a radish. It was a magic *ginseng*. The man ate it and tried to lift the stone. But it was very heavy and he could move it only with great difficulty. So the old woman gave him another radish that was really a magic *ginseng*, and after he ate it the man was able to lift the stone as high as his knees. He ate one more *ginseng,* and then he could lift the stone high over his head with the greatest of ease.

So the old woman gave him a big sword and said, "Go over the next hill until you find a big flat stone. Lift up that stone and you will find the entrance to a big cave. Inside the cave you will find a road which will lead you to the giant's home. With the strength you have now acquired I am sure you will be able to kill him."

So the man went over the hill and found the big flat stone just as the old woman had said. He lifted it up and went into the cave.

There he found an underground world.

At first the road was very narrow, but before long it widened. And at last he came out into the open, in front of a big tiled house surrounded by a wall with nine gates. He went in through one of the gates and climbed a willow tree which stood beside a well. He stayed hidden in the branches to see what would happen.

Soon a girl came to the well, carrying a water jar on her head. She drew a gourd full of water from the well and sighed, "Oh when shall we see our home again?"

The man saw from his hiding place that she was the maidservant who had been carried off with his wife.

When she had filled her jar with water, the man dropped a few leaves into it.

"It seems very windy today" the girl grumbled. And she poured out the water and filled her jar again.

When it was full, the man again dropped leaves into it. Once more the girl complained of the wind and once more she emptied her jar and filled it with fresh water.

Again the man dropped leaves into the jar.

This time the girl looked up and saw her master hidden in the branches of the willow tree. She was overjoyed to see him and called to him to come down.

"The giant is away just now," she said. "Wait here while I go and tell the mistress."

So she went to tell his wife who came running to greet him.

The man's wife told him all about the horrible giant. "His habits are strange," she said. "He goes away for three months and ten days, and then comes back and sleeps for three months and three days. He has been gone just ten days and will return three months from now. Until then, you had better drink *zanggun-su,* 'the general's drink,' so that you will gain enough strength to overcome him."

Then the woman led her husband to a cave with a

34

stone door. Inside the cave was a spring of crystal clear water. The man drank this water every day for a week. At the end of that time, his wife brought him a big sword and said, "This is the giant's sword. Are you strong enough to use it?"

The man tried, but the sword was too heavy. So he continued to drink water from the spring, and by the end of the first month he became so strong he could flourish the sword with the greatest of ease.

When two months had gone by, he could wear the giant's wooden shoes and leap high in the air in them.

And at the end of three months he was so strong he could wear the heavy helmet and armor of the giant and carry the giant's two swords at one time.

Now it was time for the giant to return. One day there was a deafening thunderclap and the nine-headed giant strode into the house through the main gate. He scowled and roared, "I smell a man."

The man's wife answered, "Nonsense! But you must be very thirsty after your journey, and I have some excellent wine for you. Do drink some and relax."

She had prepared especially strong wine for this very purpose and the giant drank nine barrels of it— one barrel with each head.

When he had finished, he lay down at once and fell into a drunken sleep.

Now the man came into the room. He was wearing the giant's armor, and the giant's wooden leaping shoes, and he was carrying the two heavy swords.

The giant's body was covered with scales as hard as iron, so that there was no place to thrust the swords. But the man kicked the giant hard on the shin and this made all the scales stand up on end. Now the man could thrust his swords into one of the necks of the giant.

The giant started up with a groan and lashed out furiously. He leaped high in the air and the man followed him. High in the clouds they joined in mortal combat.

The two women on the ground could not see them, but the clash of steel rang in their ears. They trembled in fear, and prayed that the giant might be overcome.

Before long, three of the giant's heads fell crashing to the ground. Rolling their eyes in fury, the heads sprang back into the air to join the giant's body. And as they went they cursed, "You hateful women, to deceive me thus!" And so the desperate struggle continued high in the air.

Then the women went and brought ashes in their

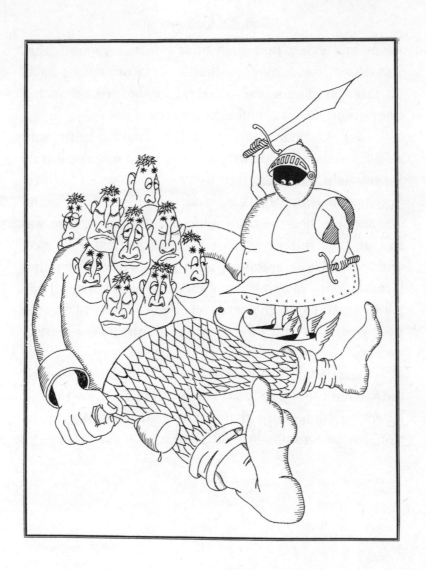

skirts and every time a head fell to the ground, they smothered it with ashes so that it could not spring back. At last the giant's body crashed to the ground with a heavy thud and lay lifeless before them.

Then the man came down, his face dripping with sweat. He thanked his wife and her maid most profusely for the help they had given him.

Next morning the man and his wife and the maid-servant searched the dead giant's storehouses. One was full of gold and silver; another was heaped with rice, and a third was crammed with silk. They also found human bones hanging from the rafters and two of the giant's victims on the point of death. They untied the poor prisoners and offered them all the treasure they wanted.

Then they all set out for home. When they reached the village there was great celebration, for now the villagers could be sure that never again would they be troubled by the nine-headed giant.

David and Goliath

Here is a story of little David and the giant Goliath as the Bible tells it.

How tall was Goliath? Six cubits and a span, says the Bible. And how tall is that? Well, before there were tape measures, people used to use their hands and arms and feet as units of measure. A cubit is the length of a man's forearm—from the elbow to the tip of the middle finger. Scholars tell us that a Hebrew cubit was about $17\frac{1}{2}$ inches—17.58 inches, to be exact. And a span is the distance from the end of a man's thumb to the end of his little finger when he stretches his hand—about 9 inches.

Figured out in feet and inches:

$$1 \text{ cubit} = 17.58 \text{ inches}$$
$$\times 6$$
$$6 \text{ cubits} = \overline{105.48 \text{ inches}}$$
$$1 \text{ span} = +9.00 \text{ inches}$$
$$\overline{114.48 \text{ inches}}$$

Now divide by 12 to get the number of feet—9.54. That is, Goliath was about 9½ feet tall.

Now the Philistines gathered together their armies to battle. And Saul and the men of Israel were gathered together, and pitched by the valley of Elah, and set the battle in array against the Philistines. And the Philistines stood on a mountain on the one side, and Israel stood on a mountain on the other side, and there was a valley between them.

And there went out a champion out of the camp of the Philistines, named Goliath, of Gath, whose height was six cubits and a span. And he had an helmet of brass upon his head, and he was armed with a coat of mail; and the weight of the coat was five thousand shekels of brass. And he had greaves of brass upon his legs, and a target of brass between his shoulders. And the staff of his spear was like a weaver's beam; and his spear's head weighed six hundred shekels of iron; and one bearing a shield went before him.

And he stood and cried unto the armies of Israel, and said unto them, "Why are ye come out to set your battle in array? Am not I a Philistine, and ye servants to Saul? Choose you a man for you, and let him come down to me. If he be able to fight with me, and to kill me, then will we be your servants; but if I prevail against him, and kill him, then shall ye be our servants, and serve us." And the Philistine said, "I defy the armies of Israel this day. Give me a man, that we may fight together."

When Saul and all Israel heard those words of the Philistine, they were dismayed, and greatly afraid.

Now David was the son of that Ephrathite of Bethlehem-judah, whose name was Jesse; and he had eight sons. And David was the youngest. And the three eldest followed Saul to the battle. But David went and returned from Saul to feed his father's sheep at Bethlehem.

And the Philistine drew near morning and evening, and presented himself forty days.

And Jesse said unto David, his son, "Take now for

thy brethren an ephah of this parched corn, and these ten loaves, and run to the camp to thy brethren. And carry these ten cheeses unto the captain of their thousand, and look how thy brethren fare, and take their pledge."

And David rose up early in the morning, and left the sheep with a keeper, and took, and went, as Jesse had commanded him; and he came to the trench as the host was going forth to the fight, and shouted for the battle; for Israel and the Philistines had put the battle in array, army against army.

And David left his carriage in the hand of the keeper of the carriage, and ran into the army, and came and saluted his brethren. And as he talked with them, behold, there came up the champion, the Philistine of Gath, Goliath by name, out of the armies of the Philistines, and spake according to the same words, and David heard them.

And all the men of Israel, when they saw the man, fled from him, and were sore afraid. And the men of Israel said, "Have ye seen this man that is come up? Surely to defy Israel is he come up. And it shall be, that the man who killeth him, the king will enrich him with great riches, and will give him his daughter, and make his father's house free in Israel."

And David spake to the men that stood by him, say-ing, "What shall be done to the man that killeth this Philistine, and taketh away the reproach from Israel? For who is this uncircumcised Philistine, that he should defy the armies of the living God?" And the people answered him after this manner, saying, "So shall it be done to the man that killeth him."

And Eliab his eldest brother heard when he spake unto the men; and Eliab's anger was kindled against David, and he said, "Why camest thou down hither? And with whom hast thou left those few sheep in the wilderness? I know thy pride, and the haughtiness of thine heart; for thou art come down that thou mightest see the battle."

And David said, "What have I now done? Is there not a cause?" And when the words were heard which David spake, they rehearsed them before Saul: and he sent for him.

And David said to Saul, "Let no man's heart fail be-cause of him; thy servant will go and fight with this Philistine." And Saul said to David, "Thou art not able to go against this Philistine to fight with him: for thou art but a youth, and he a man of war from his youth."

And David said unto Saul, "Thy servant kept his father's sheep, and there came a lion, and a bear, and took a lamb out of the flock: and I went out after him, and smote him, and delivered it out of his mouth: and when he arose against me, I caught him by his beard, and smote him, and slew him. Thy servant slew both the lion and the bear: and this uncircumcised Philistine shall be as one of them, seeing he hath defied the armies of the living God." David said moreover, "The Lord that delivered me out of the paw of the lion, and out of the paw of the bear, he will deliver me out of the hand of this Philistine."

And Saul said unto David, "Go and the Lord be with thee."

And Saul armed David with his armor, and he put an helmet of brass upon his head; also he armed him with a coat of mail. And David girded his sword upon his armor, and he assayed to go. And David said unto Saul, "I cannot go with these; for I have not proved them." And David put them off him.

And he took his staff in his hand, and chose him five smooth stones out of the brook, and put them in a shepherd's bag which he had, even in a scrip; and his sling was in his hand. And he drew near to the Philistine.

44

And the Philistine came on and drew near unto David; and the man that bare the shield went before him. And when the Philistine looked about, and saw David, he disdained him, for he was but a youth, and ruddy, and of a fair countenance.

And the Philistine said unto David, "Am I a dog, that thou comest to me with staves?" And the Philistine cursed David by his gods. And the Philistine said to David, "Come to me, and I will give thy flesh unto the fowls of the air, and to the beasts of the field."

Then said David to the Philistine, "Thou comest to me with a sword, and with a spear, and with a shield. But I come to thee in the name of the Lord of hosts, the God of the armies of Israel, whom thou hast defied. This day will the Lord deliver thee into mine hand; and I will smite thee and take thine head from thee. And I will give the carcasses of the host of the Philistines this day unto the fowls of the air, and to the wild beasts of the earth; that all the earth may know that there is a God in Israel. And all this assembly shall know that the Lord saveth not with sword and spear. For the battle is the Lord's, and he will give you into our hands."

And it came to pass, when the Philistine arose, and came and drew nigh to meet David, that David hasted, and ran toward the army to meet the Philistine. And David put his hand in his bag, and took thence a stone, and slang it, and smote the Philistine in his forehead, that the stone sunk into his forehead; and he fell upon his face to the earth.

So David prevailed over the Philistine with a sling and with a stone, and smote the Philistine, and slew him; but there was no sword in the hand of David. Therefore David ran, and stood upon the Philistine, and took his sword, and drew it out of the sheath thereof, and cut off his head therewith. And when the Philistines saw their champion was dead, they fled.

And the men of Israel and of Judah arose, and shouted, and pursued the Philistines. And David took the head of the Philistine and brought it to Jerusalem.

—*I Samuel, 17*

PEOPLE WHO BELIEVED IN GIANTS USED TO SAY—

THUNDER—is the sound of a giant laughing.

46

Tricky Giants and Giant-trickers

The Three Brothers and the Giant

How is a French giant different from an English giant? Well, he speaks French, of course. (But I have translated everything into English for you in this story of three French boys and a French giant.) In all other ways, the giant in this story is very much like the English giants you have met. He likes to eat children, he drinks too much wine, and he's not very bright. His name is Barbe d'Or, which means Gold-beard.

A poor woman had three sons, each more lively and full of mischief than the next one. Their names were Jean, Jeannot, and Jeannois.

One day the woman took her three sons to the forest

nearby to help her gather firewood for the winter. The boys, soon tiring of the work, slipped away from their mother and went hunting for berries and nuts.

They went deeper and deeper into the forest, and as night closed in on them, the boys realized they were lost. Foxes were yapping, owls were hooting, wolves were howling. The boys were terrified.

"What can we do?" they asked each other.

At last Jean had an idea. He climbed to the top of a great oak tree to look around, and far off he saw a light shining. "There must be a cottage there," thought Jean, and he hurried down to tell his brothers.

They walked as quickly as they could in the direction of the light, and soon they were out of the forest and standing before a great palace which had a single light shining in the window.

Boldly, Jean knocked at the door.

"Knock-knock."

"Who is there at this late hour?"

"We are three brothers lost in the forest. Will you let us spend the night here?"

A young woman opened the door just a crack. "Don't you know," she said, "that this is the palace of Gold-beard, the giant? He is out now, but he will come home soon. And he will very likely kill you and eat you as he has done to many young boys before you. Take my advice and run away as fast as you can."

"But madam," said Jean, "where can we go on this dark night? Please hide us somewhere. Tomorrow at dawn we will leave and the giant will never know we were here."

The woman took pity on the boys, so she let them come in and led them down to the cellar where she gave them some cookies, for they were very hungry. They had scarcely taken a bite when they heard the steps of the giant approaching the palace.

"Quick! Hide behind that wine barrel!" whispered the woman. Then she came up the stairs to greet the giant as though nothing had happened.

Now Gold-beard had walked many miles that day, and was terribly thirsty. "I shall just go down to the cellar to get some wine," he said. And there was nothing the woman could do or say to stop him.

"Hah! I smell fresh meat," muttered the giant as he came near the barrel where the boys were hiding. Then he lifted the great barrel as though it were a mug and emptied it in one gulp. As he threw down the empty barrel it fell against Jeannois who let out a cry of pain.

"Aha!" said the giant. "Didn't I say I smelled fresh meat? Yum! What a delicious breakfast I'll have tomorrow!" Gold-beard smacked his lips. Then with one hand he grabbed the three unlucky boys and took them upstairs to the kitchen to kill them.

But the woman heard the giant's words and quickly hid his knife. The giant searched for it in vain. "Well, never mind," he said. "I'll lose nothing by waiting till morning. Woman, take these three children to my daughters' room and put them to bed."

Trembling with fear, the woman obeyed.

It was quite late and soon everyone in the palace was in bed.

But not everyone was sleeping!

Jeannot was trying to think of some way to save himself and his brothers. "We're really in a bad way," he said to himself. And he got out of bed to take a look at the giant's daughters.

In the moonlight he saw three crowns shining, for each of the giant's daughters wore a little golden crown.

"What if Gold-beard decides to come and kill us tonight?" Jeannot said. And he moved closer to the golden crowns.

"And what if I just took these crowns and put them

on our heads?" And Jeannot reached out and took the three crowns and put one on his own head, and one on Jean's head. And the third crown he put on the head of little Jeannois.

"Now," Jeannot said, "if the giant comes to kill us, he may very well make a mistake and kill his own daughters instead." Then all three boys lay very quiet and pretended to be asleep.

Now the giant had drunk too much and was so restless he could not sleep. So he decided to get up and kill the three boys.

He came into the room and walked over to the boys' bed. In the dark he reached for Jean's head in order to twist it off his neck. But when he felt the crown he drew his hand back at once. "Imbecile that I am!" said Goldbeard. "These are my own daughters! I must have the wrong bed."

So he went to the other bed and killed his own children. Then, satisfied with his night's work, the giant went back to bed.

Jean, Jeannot, and Jeannois quickly dressed and escaped through a window. They ran and walked for two days and at last they came to the capital of the kingdom. They asked to speak to the king, and when they told him of their adventures with Gold-beard the giant, the king invited the brothers to stay on at court as page boys.

As for Gold-beard the giant, imagine how surprised and angry he was when he discovered his mistake. He became meaner than ever, and for the next three years he was the terror of the countryside. Gold-beard went up and down the land killing travelers and peasants.

Many brave knights set out to fight the giant, but not one returned.

One day Jean, the oldest of the three page boys, asked the king for his oldest daughter's hand in marriage. And he asked, too, to be made a knight, now that he was old enough.

"You are old enough," said the king, "but are you brave enough? Do you remember Gold-beard the giant? Well, bring me back his golden beard, and I promise to make you a knight and to let you marry my daughter."

Jean set out at once for Gold-beard's palace. He arrived in full daylight and knocked at the palace door.

"Knock-knock."

"What do you want?"

"I have fought and beaten every giant in the land but you," said Jean. "And now I want to fight you too."

"You are very very young, my fine page boy," said the giant. "But never mind. Come into my palace. Tonight we dine, tomorrow we fight."

Jean did not have to be coaxed. He accepted the giant's invitation gladly. During dinner Jean waited until the giant's back was turned, then he quickly poured enough sleeping powder into Gold-beard's wine to put him to sleep for three days.

"To your health!" said the giant as he raised his glass.

"To your health!" said Jean.

The giant gulped down his wine and fell to the floor, sound asleep. He snored so loudly the whole palace trembled.

Without losing a moment, Jean took a pair of scissors and cut off the giant's golden beard. Two days later, Jean was back at court. The king was astonished and delighted, and, as he had agreed, he gave Jean his eldest daughter in marriage, and promised to make him a knight soon.

Not long after, Jeannot told the king, "Sire, I love your second daughter, Marie, and I think she loves me. Will you name me a knight and give me her hand in marriage?"

56

"But you have done nothing to merit such honor," said the king.

"I am ready to prove myself worthy," replied Jeannot. "Command, and I shall obey."

"Then bring me the sword of the giant you know so well," said the king.

Jeannot set out at once, and after two days' journey, he arrived at the giant's palace.

"Another page boy to rob me!" exclaimed the giant on seeing Jeannot. "I'll settle him!"

"But I'm not here to rob you," said Jeannot. "I've heard you can drink more wine than anyone in the land, and I've come to challenge you."

"Really?" said the giant.

"Really," said Jeannot. "And I think I can beat you."

"We shall see about that," said the giant. And he led the way to the wine cellar.

"Who shall drink first?" asked the giant.

"I'll let you have that honor," answered Jeannot.

Then the giant began drinking and he drank so much that he staggered and fell dead drunk to the ground.

Jeannot took the giant's sword and carried it to the

57

king, who was even more astonished than when Jean had brought the giant's beard.

Jeannot was married to the king's second daughter as agreed, but the king did not yet make him a knight.

Now only Jeannois remained without a bride.

"Sire," he said one day to the king, "I love your youngest daughter and she loves me. I ask you to give me her hand in marriage and at the same time to make me a knight."

"That's all very well," said the king. "But you must do something to deserve such an honor."

"Command, and I shall obey," said Jeannois.

"Can you bring me the giant himself in an iron cage?"

"I shall try."

So Jeannois ordered an iron carriage to be made. When it was ready, he set out for the giant's palace.

The giant was furious when he saw this third page boy at the door. "You—you atom! Scum! Worm!" shouted the giant. "What do you want?"

"Let me come in, and I'll tell you," said Jeannois.

"Another page boy come to rob me! I'll kill you!" roared the giant.

"One moment, please," said Jeannois politely. "I

have come to help you get back your golden beard and your sword. The two page boys who robbed you are all alone in a distant castle. I brought my carriage to take you to them quickly."

Once more the giant let himself be tricked. He entered the iron carriage. Jeannot locked him in and drove as fast as he could to the king's court. Gold-beard was immediately sentenced to death.

Jeannois married the king's youngest daughter. And preparations were made for a great celebration at which all three brothers were to be made Knights of the Realm. During the festivities the boys' mother came to the king's court seeking her long lost sons. Imagine her joy and that of her sons when at last they met!

Giuanni and the Giant

This amusing Italian tale of how a quick-witted woodcutter fools a giant has a theme that is a favorite in many countries. In Germany they tell a story something like this about a tailor. In Greece the hero is a cobbler. In Ireland it is a lazy good-for-nothing boy who proves he is good for something after all.

Whatever the country and whoever the hero, the purpose of this story is to make people laugh. And if there is a moral at all, it is: *Boasting can get you into trouble, but brain work can get you out again.*

Giuanni and the Giant

In Rome there once lived a woodcutter called Giuanni. One day, while he was cutting off a branch of an oak tree, the branch fell on top of him, broke his shinbone, and he had to stay in a hospital for three months. But he didn't want to stay in the hospital, so he ran away and went to live in a small place called Marca. One day he sat down to remove the bandage from his leg, and as soon as the wound was uncovered, a swarm of flies began to buzz around the open sore. Giuanni got up and started swatting them one after the other. When there were no more left, he began to count the flies that were lying dead on the ground to see how many he had killed. They amounted to five hundred! Giuanni was proud of himself, and he made up a little sign which said:

Giuanni is my name, I'm the strongest in the land;
I felled five hundred with a single hand.

Then he tied this sign around his neck, went into town and took a room at an inn.

The next day he was called by the governor, who said to him: "Since you are the strongest in the land, I want

61

you to go up into the mountain and catch the giant who has been killing our people."

So Giuanni went into the woods and walked on and on towards the mountain until he came upon a shepherd. "Where is the giant's cave?" he asked him.

"Why do you want to go there?" said the shepherd. "He'll eat you up in one mouthful!"

And Giuanni said: "Give me three or four chunks of pot cheese, will you, and I'll pay you for them." Then he went on his way, carrying three big chunks of pot cheese under his arm.

When he reached the giant's cave, he stamped and scraped his feet to make some noise. The giant heard him and came out. "Who's there!" he said.

Giuanni took a fistful of the pot cheese in his right hand and said to the giant: "Now you be quiet or else I'll crush you to pieces like this stone in my hand," and as he squeezed the cheese, it crumbled into little pieces that slid through his fingers and fell all over the ground. When the giant saw this, his eyes widened, and he asked Giuanni if he wanted to stay with him. Giuanni said yes, threw away the rest of the pot cheese, and joined the giant in his cave.

The following morning, the giant took a long rope

and went out into the forest for some wood, and Giuanni went along with him. The giant tied the rope around the trunk of two oak trees and pulled both of them up out of the ground, roots and all. Then he said to Giuanni: "Come on now, let's see *you* pull one up."

"Sure," said Giuanni, "but tell me, giant, don't you have a rope that's a bit longer? I want to tie it around the whole forest and pull up all the trees at one time, so we don't have to bother coming back."

"What do you want to do?" said the giant. "Ruin a whole generation of trees! We have plenty of wood already, so let it go."

One day the giant made a bet with Giuanni to see who could throw farther and whoever did would win a hundred scudi. The object he chose for throwing was a large millstone which he borrowed from a nearby mill. The giant went first and he threw the great millstone a whole mile. He retrieved the millstone, marked off the spot where it landed, and then said to Giuanni: "Now it's your turn."

Looking down at that big, heavy millstone, Giuanni realized it was much too heavy for him even to budge. He leaned forward and gazed into the distance, then cried out: "Hey, you out there, yoo-hoo, look out!"

The giant squinted, and said: "Who are you shouting at? I don't see anyone out there."

And Giuanni said: "I'm calling to those people way out there by the sea. I want to warn them to clear the way."

"Well, in that case, let's forget the whole thing. If you throw the millstone that far out, we'll never be able to find it again." So he gave up and handed Giuanni the hundred scudi.

Later on, Giuanni himself suggested a test to measure their strength. "Let's see how deep you can push your finger into that oak tree over there."

"Very well," said the giant, "and I'll bet another hundred scudi."

Earlier that day, Giuanni had made a hole in the trunk of that tree with a drill and a knife, then he had refilled the hole with wood shavings so that it couldn't be seen. When the giant pushed his finger into the tree, he made a dent about two inches deep; and when Giuanni's turn came, he took aim at the hole he had made, punched into the tree, and went through all the way up to the middle of his arm.

The giant gave him the hundred scudi, but was getting very tired of having such a strong man as Giuanni around. He decided to get rid of him, and sent him away. He waited until Giuanni was half way down the side of the mountain, and then he rolled over an avalanche of huge rocks. But Giuanni, who didn't trust the giant for one minute, had hidden himself in a cave on the side of the mountain, and when he heard the rocks coming down, he shouted up to the giant: "What's this falling from the heavens? Seems like it's snowing flakes of plaster!"

The giant heard this and said to himself: "Good Heavens! I throw down a load of rocks and he calls them flakes of plaster! Better to have such a man as a friend than as an enemy." And he invited him back to his cave. But he was still thinking of a way to get rid of him. So one night, while Giuanni was asleep, he crept quietly to his bed and gave him a blow on the head. But it should be known that every night Giuanni put a pumpkin on his pillow and slept with his head at the foot of the bed. As soon as the giant squashed the pumpkin, he heard Giuanni's voice: "That you have broken my head doesn't matter much, but for having broken my sleep, you shall pay dearly!"

The giant was becoming more and more afraid of this Giuanni, and he said to himself: "I know what I'll do;

I'll take him deep into the forest and leave him there for the wolves to tear apart." So he said to Giuanni one day: "Come along, Giuanni, let's take a little walk."

"Very well," said Giuanni.

"And shall we have a little race between the two of us?" asked the giant.

"Sure," replied Giuanni. "But to be fair about it, you should give me a head start since your legs are much longer than mine."

"That's fair enough," said the giant. "I'll give you a ten-minute start."

Giuanni took off, and he ran and ran until he came to a shepherd herding his sheep. "Will you sell me one of your sheep?" he asked. The shepherd agreed; then Giuanni picked up the sheep, cut its belly open with a knife, removed the entrails, the liver, and the rest of the sheep's insides, and scattered them all over the road. Then he said to the shepherd: "If a giant comes by here and asks about me, tell him I cut out all my insides and threw them away so that I would weigh less and be able to run faster. Then say I ran like the wind, and show him the entrails here on the ground."

Ten minutes later, here came the giant, galloping along. "Have you seen a man running by?" he asked the shepherd.

The shepherd told him the story about the entrails and pointed to them on the ground. "Give me a knife," said the giant, "and I'll do the same." So he took the knife and cut open his belly from top to bottom, and he fell down to the ground and died. Giuanni, who had hidden himself in a nearby tree, jumped down, loaded the giant on to a wagon drawn by two buffaloes, and transported him into town.

When the Governor saw the dead giant, he had his body brought to the town square and burned. And he rewarded Giuanni by keeping him well fed for the rest of his life.

PEOPLE WHO BELIEVED IN GIANTS USED TO SAY—
LAKES—are a giant's footprints filled with water.

68

Why Are Giants So Stupid?

According to an ancient fable, Zeus, the chief god of the Greeks, fashioned men into a variety of sizes, from very small to gigantic.

He then told the god Hermes to pour some common sense into them all. After dividing it into small portions, Hermes poured into each man an equal quantity of the precious brew.

The dose was enough to fill the smaller men who thereupon became noted for common sense and good judgment.

But for the men of gigantic size, the portion was much too small to circulate through their great bodies. As a result, they remained rather stupid.

—Adapted from a fable of Aesop

69

Odysseus in the Land of the Giants

Three thousand years ago, the Greek poet Homer told the story of Odysseus—his wars and his wanderings. And ever since, the story has been told and retold. Here you can read about one of Odysseus' many adventures: how he was trapped in the cave of the man-eating giant Cyclops named Polyphemus; how he managed to outwit the giant and make his escape.

This is the story as Odysseus tells it to King Alcinous on whose shores he was shipwrecked. It is from the book, *The Children's Homer* where the adventures of Odysseus are retold by a poet and storyteller living today— Padraic Colum.

I am Odysseus, son of Laertes, and my land is Ithika. And I will tell you the tale of my wanderings:

After we conquered Troy, we set sail. We should soon have come to our own country, all unhurt. But the north wind came and swept us from our course.

After many days we came to the land of the Cyclopes, a giant people. There is an empty island outside the harbor of their land, and we beached our ships there and took down our sails. Then we looked across to the land of the Cyclopes, and we heard the sound of voices and heard the bleating of flocks of sheep and goats.

I called my companions together and I said, "It would be well for some of us to go to that other island. With my own ship and with the company that is on it I shall go there. The rest of you abide here. I will find out what manner of men live there, and whether they will treat us kindly and give us gifts that are due to strangers —gifts of provision for our voyage."

We embarked and came to the land. I took twelve men with me and left the rest to guard the ship. There was a cave near the sea, and we went into it, but we found no man there. There were baskets filled with cheeses, and there were pails and bowls of milk. My men wanted

71

me to take some of the cheeses and drive off some of the lambs and kids and come away. But this I would not do.

While we were in the cave, he whose dwelling it was returned to it. He carried on his shoulder a great pile of wood for his fire. Never in our lives did we see a creature so frightful as this Cyclops was. He was a giant in size. And, what made him terrible to behold, he had but one eye, and that single eye was in his forehead.

He cast down on the ground the pile of wood that he carried, making such a din that we fled in terror into the corners and recesses of the cave. Next he drove his flocks into the cave and began to milk his ewes and goats. And when he had the flocks within, he took up a stone that not all our strengths could move and set it as a door to the mouth of the cave.

The Cyclops kindled his fire, and when it blazed up he saw us.

I spoke to him and begged him to deal with us kindly, for the sake of Zeus who is ever in the company of strangers and suppliants. But he answered me saying, "We Cyclopes pay no heed to Zeus, nor to any of your gods, for we are mightier than they." And without saying another word, he laid hands upon two of my men, and swinging them by the legs, dashed their brains out on the earth. He cut them to pieces and ate them before our very eyes. We wept and we prayed to Zeus as we witnessed a deed so terrible.

Next the Cyclops stretched himself amongst his sheep and went to sleep beside the fire. Then I debated whether I should take my sharp sword in my hand and, feeling where his heart was, stab him there. But second thoughts held me back from doing this. I might be able to kill him as he slept, but not even with my companions could I roll away the great stone that closed the mouth of the cave.

Dawn came, and the Cyclops awakened, kindled his fire, and milked his flocks. Then he seized two more of my men and killed them for his midday meal. And now he rolled away the great stone and drove his flocks out of the cave.

I had pondered on a way of escape, and I had thought of something that might be done. I had with me a great skin of sweet wine, and I thought that if I could make him drunken with wine, I and my companions might be able to overcome him.

But there were other preparations to be made first. On the floor of the cave there was a great beam of olive wood which the Cyclops had cut to make a club when the wood should be seasoned. I and my companions went and cut off a fathom's length of the wood and sharpened it to a point and took it to the fire and hardened it in the glow. Then I hid the beam in the recess of the cave.

The Cyclops came back in the evening and, opening up the cave, drove in his flocks. Then he closed the cave again with the stone and went and milked his ewes and goats. Again he seized two of my companions and killed them and ate them. I went to the terrible creature with a bowl of wine in my hands. He took it and drank it and cried out, "Give me another bowl of this, and tell me your name that I may give you gifts for bringing me this honey-tasting drink."

I spoke to him guilefully and said, "*Noman* is my name. *Noman* my father and my mother call me."

"Give me more of the drink, Noman," he shouted. "And the gift that I shall give to you is that I shall make you the last of your fellows to be eaten."

I gave him wine again, and when he had taken the third bowl he sank backwards with his face upturned, and sleep came upon him. Then I, with four companions, took that beam of olive wood and thrust the point of it into the fire. When it began to glow we drew it out of the flame. Then we laid hold on the great beam and, dashing

at the sleeping Cyclops, thrust it into his eye. He raised a terrible cry that made the rocks ring and we dashed away into the recesses of the cave.

His cries brought other Cyclopes to the mouth of the

75

cave, and they, naming him as Polyphemus, called out and asked him what ailed him.

"Noman," he shrieked, "Noman is slaying me!"

They answered him saying, "If no man is slaying you, there is nothing we can do for you, Polyphemus."

And they went away.

Polyphemus then, groaning with pain, rolled away the stone and sat before the mouth of the cave with his hands outstretched, thinking that he would catch us as we dashed out. I showed my companions how we might pass by him. I laid hands on certain rams of the flock and I lashed three of them together with supple rods. Then under the middle ram I put a man of my company. Thus every three rams carried a man. As soon as dawn came, the rams hastened out to the pasture, and, as they passed, Polyphemus laid hands on the first and third of each three that went by. Polyphemus did not guess that the middle ram carried out a man.

For myself, I took a ram that was the strongest and fleeciest of the whole flock and I placed myself under him, clinging to the wool of his belly. As this ram was going out, last of all, Polyphemus laid his hands upon him.

"My sweet ram," he said, "what is the meaning of

this? Why are you the last to leave my cave—you who are always the first to lead the flock to the meadows, and the first to come home again at night? Now you are the last of all. Is it because you know your master has lost his eye? And do you grieve for him? Ah, if you could talk you would tell me where Noman is hiding, and I would dash his brains upon the ground until they flew all over the cave."

The ram went by him, and when he had gone a little way from the cave I loosed myself from him and went and set my companions free.

We gathered together many of Polyphemus' sheep and we drove them down to our ship. The men guarding the ship would have wept when they heard what happened to six of their companions. But I bade them take on board the sheep we had brought and pull the ship away from that land. Then when we had drawn a certain distance from the shore I could not forbear to shout my taunts: "Cyclops," I cried, "you thought it was a fool and a weakling whose friends you could eat. But now your evil deeds have been punished."

So I shouted, and Polyphemus came to the mouth of the cave with great anger in his heart. He tore the top off a high mountain and hurled it at the ship. The men bent to the oars and pulled the ship away. And when we were further away I shouted: "Cyclops, if any man should ask who it was set his mark upon you, say that he was Odysseus, the son of Laertes."

We went on in our ship, rejoicing at our escape. We came to the island where my other ships were. All the company rejoiced to see us, although they had to mourn for their six companions slain by Polyphemus. We divided amongst the ships the sheep we had taken from Polyphemus' flock and we sacrificed to the gods. At the dawn of the next day we raised the sails on each ship and we sailed away.

PEOPLE WHO BELIEVED IN GIANTS USED TO SAY—

SAND DUNES AND GREAT BOULDERS—show where a giant emptied sand and gravel out of his shoes.

The Clever Cat and the Giant

In a country far away, whose name I can't remember, there stands a statue of a cat. The cat lived
long ago, but he is still remembered as a national hero
who, through cleverness and courage, rid the country of
a fierce giant.

This giant had magic powers. He was able to turn
himself into any kind of creature he chose. Very often
he would turn into a huge elephant and trample the
fields, destroying all the crops. Or he would turn into a
fiery dragon and burn down houses and barns. When he
turned into a man-eating tiger, he would pounce upon
travelers and eat them.

One day the brave cat called upon the giant. "I have come," said the cat, "to pay my respects to the cleverest and most powerful giant ever known."

The giant accepted the compliment with an ill-humored grunt. The cat could see the giant was flattered, however, and went on to say, "Is it really true that you can change into any creature you choose? That is hard to believe."

Without saying a word, the giant turned himself into a fiery dragon. The cat jumped back just in time to prevent his whiskers from being singed. "Well," said the cat as soon at the giant returned to his usual shape, "seeing is believing! Still, to change from a great giant into a great dragon is only moderately remarkable. Can you, by any chance, turn into something very small—a mouse, for example?"

Again the giant said nothing. He simply sneezed—and turned himself into a field mouse. At once the clever cat pounced upon the mouse and ate it. And that was the end of the mouse—and of the giant, too.

The Giant Who Had
No Heart in His Body

Now how can you kill a giant if he has no heart in his body? And if the giant's heart is not in his body, where is it? That is what the hero of this fairy tale from Scandinavia must find out!

Once on a time there was a king who had seven sons, and he loved them so much that he could never bear to be without them all at once, but one must always be with him. Now when they were grown up, six were to set off to woo. But as for the youngest, his father kept him at home, and the others were to bring back a princess for him to the palace. So the king gave the six the finest clothes you ever set eyes on, so fine that the light gleamed from them a long way off. And each had his horse, which cost many, many hundred dollars. And so they set off. Now, when they had been to many palaces, and seen many princesses, at last they came to a king who had six daughters. Such lovely king's daughters they had never seen, and so they fell to wooing them, each one. And when they had got them for sweethearts, they set off home again. But they quite forgot that they were to bring back with them a sweetheart for Boots, their brother, for they were over head and ears in love with their own sweethearts.

But when they had gone a good bit on their way, they passed close by a steep hillside, like a wall, where the giant's house was. And there the giant came out and turned them all into stone, princes and princesses and all. Now, the king waited and waited for his six sons, but the more he waited, the longer they stayed away; the king was sorely troubled and said he should never know what it was to be glad again.

82

"And if I had not you left," he said to Boots, "I would live no longer, so full of sorrow am I for the loss of your brothers."

"Well, but now I've been thinking to ask your leave to set out and find them again. That's what I'm thinking of," said Boots.

"Nay, nay!" said his father. "That leave you shall never get, for then you would stay away too."

But Boots had set his heart upon it. Go he would. And he begged and prayed so long that the king was forced to let him go. Now, you must know the king had no other horse to give Boots but an old broken-down jade, for his six other sons and their train had carried off all his horses; but Boots did not care a pin for that. He sprang up on his sorry old steed.

"Farewell, father," said Boots. "I'll come back, never fear. And like enough I shall bring my six brothers back with me." And with that he rode off.

So when he had ridden a while, he came to a raven that lay in the road and flapped its wings, and was not able to get out of the way, it was so starved.

"Oh, dear friend," said the raven, "give me a little food, and I'll help you again at your utmost need."

"I haven't much food," said the prince, "and I don't

see how you'll ever be able to help me much. But still I can spare you a little. I see you want it."

So he gave the raven some of the food he had brought with him.

Now, when he had gone a bit farther, he came to a brook. And in the brook lay a great salmon which had got upon a dry place and dashed itself about, and could not get into the water again.

"Oh, dear friend," said the salmon to the prince, "shove me out into the water, and I'll help you again at your utmost need."

"Well," said the prince, "the help you'll give me will not be great, I dare say, but it's a pity you should lie there and choke." And with that he shot the fish out into the stream again.

After that he went a long, long way, and he met a wolf that was so famished it lay and crawled along the road on its belly.

"Dear friend, do let me have your horse," said the wolf. "I'm so hungry the wind whistles through my ribs. I've had nothing to eat these two years."

"No," said Boots, "this will never do. First I came to a raven, and I was forced to give him my food; next I came to a salmon, and him I had to help into the water

again; and now you will have my horse. It can't be done, that it can't, for then I should have nothing to ride on."

"Nay, dear friend, but you can help me," said Graylegs the wolf. "You can ride upon my back, and I'll help you again in your utmost need."

"Well, the help I shall get from you will not be great, I'll be bound," said the prince. "But you may take my horse, since you are in such need."

So when the wolf had eaten the horse, Boots took the bit and put it into the wolf's jaw, and laid the saddle on his back. And now the wolf was so strong, after what he had got inside, that he set off with the prince like nothing. So fast the prince had never ridden before.

"When we have gone a bit farther, I'll show you the giant's house," said Graylegs, "and there you will see what has become of your brothers."

So after a while they came to it.

"See, here is the giant's house," said the wolf. "And see, here are your six brothers, whom the giant has turned into stone. And see, here are their six brides. And away yonder is the door, and in that door you must go."

"Nay, but I daren't go in," said the prince. "He'll take my life."

"No! no!" said the wolf. "When you get in you'll find a princess, and she'll tell you what to do to make an end of the giant. Only mind and do as she bids you."

Well, Boots went in, but, truth to say, he was very much afraid. When he came in, the giant was away, but in one of the rooms sat the princess, just as the wolf had said. And so lovely a princess, Boots had never yet set eyes on.

"Oh! Heaven help you! Whence have you come?" said the princess, as she saw him. "It will surely be your death. No one can make an end of the giant who lives here, for he has no heart in his body."

"Well! well!" said Boots, "but now that I am here, I may as well try what I can do with him. And I will see if

86

I can't free my brothers, who are standing turned to stone out of doors. And you, too, I will try to save, that I will."

"Well, if you must, you must," said the princess. "And so let us see if we can't hit on a plan. Just creep under the bed yonder, and mind and listen to what he and I talk about. But, pray, do lie as still as a mouse."

So he crept under the bed, and he had scarce got well underneath it, before the giant came.

"Ha!" roared the giant, "what a smell of Christian blood there is in the house!"

"Yes, I know there is," said the princess, "for there came a magpie flying with a man's bone, and let it fall down the chimney. I made all the haste I could to get it out, but for all one can do, the smell doesn't go off so soon."

So the giant said no more about it, and when night came, he went to bed.

After a while, the princess said: "There is one thing I'd be so glad to ask you about, if only I dared."

"What thing is that?" asked the giant.

"Only where it is you keep your heart, since you don't carry it about you," said the princess.

"Ah! That's a thing you've no business to ask about.

87

But if you must know, it lies under the door-sill," said the giant.

"Ho! ho!" said Boots to himself under the bed, "then we'll soon see if we can't find it."

Next morning the giant got up early, and strode off to the wood. But he was hardly out of the house before Boots and the princess set to work to look under the door-sill for his heart. But the more they dug, and the more they hunted, the more they couldn't find it.

"He has balked us this time," said the princess, "but we'll try him once more."

So she picked all the prettiest flowers she could find, and strewed them over the door-sill which they had laid in its right place again. And when the time came for the giant to come home, Boots crept under the bed. Just as he was well under, back came the giant.

Snuff—snuff, went the giant's nose. "My eyes and limbs, what a smell of Christian blood there is in here," said he.

"I know there is," said the princess, "for there came a magpie flying with a man's bone in his bill, and let it fall down the chimney. I made as much haste as I could to get it out, but I dare say it's that you smell."

So the giant held his peace, and said no more about

it. A little while after, he asked who it was that had strewed flowers about the door-sill.

"Oh, I, of course," said the princess.

"And pray, what's the meaning of all this?" said the giant.

"Ah!" said the princess, "I'm so fond of you that I couldn't help strewing them, when I knew that your heart lay under there."

"You don't say so," said the giant; "but after all it doesn't lie there at all."

So when he went to bed again in the evening, the princess asked the giant again where his heart was, for she said she would so like to know.

"Well," said the giant, "if you must know, it lies away yonder in the cupboard against the wall."

"So, so!" thought Boots and the princess; "then we'll soon try to find it."

Next morning the giant was away early, and strode off to the wood. And so soon as he was gone Boots and the princess were in the cupboard hunting for his heart, but the more they sought for it the less they found it.

"Well," said the princess, "we'll just try him once more."

So she decked out the cupboard with flowers and

garlands, and when the time came for the giant to come home, Boots crept under the bed again.

Then back came the giant.

Snuff—snuff! "My eyes and limbs, what a smell of Christian blood there is in here!"

"I know there is," said the princess, "for a little while since there came a magpie flying with a man's bone in his bill, and let it fall down the chimney. I made all the haste I could to get it out of the house again. But after all my pains, I dare say it's that you smell."

When the giant heard that, he said no more about it. But a little while after, he saw how the cupboard was all decked about with flowers and garlands, so he asked who it was that had done that? Who could it be but the princess.

"And pray, what's the meaning of all this tomfoolery?" asked the giant.

"Oh, I'm so fond of you, I couldn't help doing it when I knew your heart lay there," said the princess.

"How can you be so silly as to believe any such thing?" said the giant.

"Oh, yes; how can I help believing it, when you say it?" said the princess.

"You're a goose," said the giant; "where my heart

is, you will never come."

"Well," said the princess; "but for all that, 'twould be such a pleasure to know where it really lies."

The poor giant could hold out no longer, but was forced to say:

"Far, far away in a lake lies an island. On that island stands a church. In that church is a well. In that well swims a duck. In that duck there is an egg. And in that egg lies my heart—you darling!"

In the morning early the giant strode off to the wood.

"Yes! Now I must set off too," said Boots. "If I only knew how to find the way." He took a long, long farewell of the princess, and when he got out of the giant's door, there stood the wolf waiting for him. So Boots told him all that had happened inside the house, and said now he wished to ride to the well in the church, if he only knew the way. So the wolf bade him jump on his back, and he'd soon find the way. And away they went till the wind whistled after them, over hedge and field, over hill and dale. After they had traveled many, many days, they came at last to the lake. Then the prince did not know how to get over it, but the wolf bade him only not be afraid, but stick on. And so he jumped into the lake with the prince on his back, and swam over to the island. So they came to the church. But the church keys hung high, high up on the top of the tower, and at first the prince did not know how to get them down.

"You must call on the raven," said the wolf.

So the prince called on the raven, and immediately the raven came, and flew up and fetched the keys. And so the prince got into the church. But when he came to the well, there lay the duck, and swam about backwards and forwards, just as the giant had said. So the prince stood and coaxed it and coaxed it, till it came to him, and he grasped it in his hand. But just as he lifted it up from the water the duck dropped the egg into the well, and then Boots was beside himself to know how to get it out again. "Well, now you must call on the salmon, to be sure," said the wolf. And the king's son called on the salmon, and the salmon came and fetched up the egg from the bottom of the well.

The wolf told him to squeeze the egg, and as soon as ever he squeezed it the giant screamed out.

"Squeeze it again," said the wolf; and when the prince did so, the giant screamed still more piteously, and begged and prayed to be spared, saying he would do all that the prince wished if he would only not squeeze his heart in two.

92

"Tell him he must restore to life again your six brothers and their brides, whom he has turned to stone," said the wolf. Yes, the giant was ready to do that, and he turned the six brothers into king's sons again, and their brides into king's daughters.

"Now, squeeze the egg in two," said the wolf. So Boots squeezed the egg to pieces, and the giant burst at once.

Now, when he had made an end of the giant, Boots rode back again on the wolf to the giant's house, and there stood all his six brothers alive and merry, with their brides. Then Boots went into the hillside after his bride, and so they all set off home to their father's house. And you may fancy how glad the old king was when he saw all his seven sons come back, each with his bride.

"But the loveliest bride of all is the bride of Boots," said the king, "and he shall sit uppermost at the table, with her by his side."

So he sent out, and called a great wedding feast, and the mirth was both loud and long. And if they have not done feasting, why they are at it still.

Thor and the Giants

Long long ago, in the land of the Norsemen, the gods and giants were at war with each other.

The gods lived in Asgard, far above Mitgard, the kingdom of men; far above Jotunheim, the kingdom of the giants. The mighty giants were enemies of all that was good. But the gods were the friends and protectors of men.

One of the strongest and noblest of the gods was Thor, the god of thunder. (Our fifth day of the week, Thursday—"Thor's day"—is named after him.) Thor liked to travel through the heavens in his chariot drawn by two magic goats. And when the men of the Kingdom of Mitgard heard the roar of thunder and saw the lightning flash, they said, "That is Thor, riding across the heavens in his chariot."

One day, Thor decided to leave Asgard and journey down through the kingdom of men and then to Jotunheim, the kingdom of the giants. He would try his strength with the giants, Thor thought. He would challenge the giants to a contest. And if he could prove he was stronger, then perhaps the giants would not do so many evil deeds.

This is the story of that contest—one of the strangest ever held.

One morning, just as the sun was beginning to shine through the mists that overhung the world, the gates of Asgard opened and Thor's chariot, drawn by the goats, rattled along the road. Thor had brought Loke with him to keep him company.

All day long the chariot rolled across the meadows and through the valleys. At night it stopped at the house of a poor peasant, and Thor stepped down and stood in the doorway.

"Can you lodge two travelers overnight?" he asked.

"Certainly," said the peasant, "but we can give you nothing to eat, for we have nothing for ourselves."

"Give yourselves no trouble about that," answered Thor cheerfully. "I can provide for all."

He went back to Loke, who got out of the chariot. And then, to the great astonishment of the people in the

house, Thor killed both his goats, and in a minute they
were ready for cooking. The great pot was soon sending
savory odors through the house, and the whole family
with their strange guests sat down to a bountiful supper.

"The more you eat the better I shall like it," said
Thor, as they took their places at the table, "but do not
on any account break the bones. When you have done
with them, throw them into the skins which I have spread
out on the hearth."

The peasant and his wife, and Thialfe and Roskva,
their two children, ate ravenously. When no one was
looking, Thialfe broke one of the bones to get the
marrow.

The next morning Thor was up with the sun, and
after dressing himself he took his magic hammer and
held it over the goatskins. At once the bones flew into
place and the skins covered them, and there were the
two goats as full of life as when they started out the day
before. But one of the goats limped. And when Thor saw
it he was so angry that he looked like a thundercloud.

Thialfe, who had been watching with the rest of the
family in speechless wonder was frightened half out of
his wits when he saw Thor's rage. The poor peasant and
his wife were equally terrified, and begged Thor not to

destroy them. Seeing them in such misery, Thor forgot
his anger and said he would forgive them, but that
Thialfe must henceforth be his servant.

So taking Thialfe with them, and leaving the goats
with Thialfe's parents for safe keeping, Thor and Loke
set out again for Jotunheim, this time on foot. All morning they traveled eastward until they reached the shore
of the sea. They crossed the wide waters quickly and
climbed up on the further shore of Jotunheim. Mists
floated over the land, and great rocks rose along the
coast, so stern and black that they seemed like strong
giants guarding their country against the giant-queller.

Thor and his companions pushed on as fast as they
could until suddenly a great walled city rose before
them on a vast plain. A great gate, heavily barred,
stopped them at the entrance. But they crept between
the bars. After going a little distance, they came upon a
palace. They went through the open doors and found
themselves inside a great hall with long seats on either
side.

On these seats sat rows of gigantic men. When Thor
and his companions saw Utgard-Loke, who was the king
of the giants' country, they saluted him. But he sat for
a long time without taking any notice of them. At last,

smiling contemptuously, he said, "It is tiresome for travelers to be asked about a long journey. But if I am not mistaken, this little fellow is Thor. What feats of strength can you show us? No one is permitted to stay here unless he excels in some difficult thing."

Hearing these words in a very insulting tone, Loke answered loudly, "There is one feat in which no one can equal me, and I am ready to perform it at once. I can devour food faster than anyone here."

"Truly, that would be a feat if you could do it," said the scornful king. And he called to a man named Loge to contend with Loke.

A great wooden trough full of meat was placed in the center of the hall, and, commencing at either end, the contestants began to eat voraciously, and so fast that it is disagreeable even to think of it. They reached the middle of the trough at exactly the same moment. But Loke had eaten only the meat, while Loge had devoured meat, bones, trough, and all. There was nothing left on his side, and Loke had to confess himself beaten.

Then the king looked at Thialfe and asked, "What can you do, young man?"

"I will run a race with anyone you choose," answered Thialfe promptly.

"If you can outrun anyone I choose it will certainly be a splendid feat," said Utgard-Loke; "but you must be very swift-footed to do it."

There was a noble race-ground just outside the palace, and every one hurried out to see the race. The king called a slender young fellow name Huge, and told him to run with Thialfe.

There was never such running since the world began. Thialfe ran like the wind. But Huge reached the goal first, and turned about to meet Thialfe as he came breathless to the post.

"You must use your legs better than that if you intend to win," said the king, as Thialfe walked back, "although you are the fastest runner that ever came here."

And now it was Thor's turn to show his wonderful strength.

"Your fame fills all the world, Thor," called out Utgard-Loke, when they had seated themselves on the benches along the great wall. "Give us some proof of your wonderful power."

Thor never waited to be asked a second time.

"I will contend in drinking with anyone you may select," he said promptly.

"Well answered," said the king. "Bring out the great horn."

A giant went out and speedily came back bearing a very deep horn, which the king said his men were compelled to empty as a punishment.

"A good drinker will empty this horn at a single draught," said Utgard-Loke, as he handed it to Thor. "A few men need to drink twice, but only a milksop needs a third pull at it."

Thor thought the horn not over-large, although very long, and as he was thirsty he put it to his lips without further ado. He drank so long and deep that he thought it certainly must be empty. But when he set the horn down and looked into it, he was astonished to find that the liquor rose almost as high as when he set his lip to it.

"That was fairly well drunk," said the king, "but not unusually so. If anybody had told me Thor could do no better than that, I would not have believed him. But of course you will finish it at a second draught."

Thor said nothing, although he was very angry. He set the horn to his lips a second time and drank longer and deeper than before. When he stopped to take a breath and looked at it again, he had drunk less than the first time.

"How now, Thor," cried Utgard-Loke, "you have left more for the third draught than you can manage. If there are no other feats which you can perform better than this, you must not expect to be considered as great here as among the gods."

Thor became very angry when he heard these words and seizing the horn, he drank deep, fast, and furiously until he thought it certainly must be empty. But when he looked into the horn, the liquor had fallen so little that he could hardly see the difference. Thor handed the horn to the cup-bearer and would drink no more.

"It is plain," spoke up the king in a very insulting tone, "that you are not so strong as we thought you were. Will you try something else?"

"I will certainly try something else," said Thor, who could not understand why he had failed to drain the horn. "What game do you propose now?"

"Oh a very easy one," replied the king, "which my youngsters here make nothing of—simply to lift a cat from the floor. I should not think of asking you to try it if I did not see that you are much less of a man than I have always supposed."

He had no sooner said this than a large gray cat ran out into the hall. Thor put his hand under it and tried to

101

lift it, but the cat arched its back as high as Thor stretched his hands and, do his best, Thor could get only one of the cat's feet off the floor.

"It is just as I expected," cried Utgard-Loke in a loud voice. "The cat is very large and Thor is a very little fellow compared with the rest of us."

Thor's eyes flashed fire. "Little as I am," he shouted, "I challenge any of you to wrestle with me!"

Utgard-Loke looked up and down the benches as if he would call out someone from the two rows of giants. Then he shook his head, saying, "There is no one here who would not think it child's play to wrestle with you. But let someone call in Ellie, my old nurse. She shall try her strength with you. She has brought many a stronger man to earth."

An old woman came creeping into the hall. She was bent, wrinkled, and toothless. Thor seized her, but the tighter his grasp became, the firmer she stood. Her thin arms gripped him like a vise. Her strength seemed to grow as she put it forth, and at last, after a hard struggle, Thor sank on one knee.

"That is enough," said Utgard-Loke, and the old woman crept feebly out of the hall, leaving Thor stunned and bewildered in the midst of the silent giants.

There were no more trials of strength, and Thor and his companions were generously feasted after their defeats.

The next morning, they started on their journey homeward. Utgard-Loke went with them as far as the gate of the city, where he stopped.

"How do you think your journey has turned out?" he asked Thor. "Have you met any men stronger than yourself?"

"I have brought shame upon myself," answered Thor frankly and honestly, after his nature, "and it vexes me to think that you will hereafter speak of me as a weak fellow."

"Now that you are out of the city, I will tell you the truth about these things," said Utgard-Loke. "If I had known how mighty you are, I would never have allowed you to enter the gates, and you may be sure you will never get in a second time. I have beaten you by deception, not by strength. I have deluded you in all the trials of strength and skill.

"Loke was very hungry and ate voraciously, but he contended against fire itself, which goes like the wind and devours everything in its path.

"Thialfe ran as man never ran before. But Huge, who raced with him, was no other than my thought, and what man is so swift as thought?

"The horn which you strove in vain to empty had its further end in the sea, and so mighty were your draughts that over the wide seas the waters have sunk to the ebb.

"Your strength was no less wonderful when you lifted the cat. When we saw one foot raised from the floor our hearts sank in terror, for it was the Mitgard-serpent, encircling the whole earth, which you really contended against, and you held it aloft so near heaven that the world was hardly enclosed by its folds.

"Most marvelous of all was the wrestling with Ellie, who was none other than old age itself, who sooner or later must bring all things to the ground.

"We must part—I hope never to meet again. For I can defend myself against you only by spells of magic such as these."

Thor was so enraged when he heard these words that he swung his hammer high in the air to crush Utgard-Loke. But the king of the giants had vanished, and when Thor turned to look for the city, he saw only a beautiful plain spreading its blossoming meadows to the far mountains. So he went thoughtfully back to Asgard.

—Norse Stories *by Hamilton Wright Mabie*

Halde Hat and Dulde Hat

Now you know that a clever boy can overcome a not-so-clever giant. But suppose the giant is also a mountain king, with many other giants at his command. And suppose this same giant has a magic hat that makes him invisible. It would take a bold, quick-thinking lad to outwit a giant like that.

There was indeed, in times gone by, a giant king who had a great castle called Grimslott high up in the Borgasa Mountain. His name was Grim. He was, like the rest of his kind, ugly and crafty. And he robbed mankind of whatever fell in his way.

To help him rob and steal, he had two magic hats.

First there was the Dulde Hat. When the giant king put the Dulde Hat on his head, he became invisible, and all his giant companions became invisible too. In this way they could rob and steal to their hearts' content, and no one could lay a hand on them.

Then there was the Halde Hat. Whoever wore the Halde Hat could see whatever was hidden or invisible to others. In this way the giant king could seek out hidden treasure.

Now it happened during those times that a farmer of Grimland was preparing a wedding for his daughter, and he invited guests from near and far to the wedding feast. But no invitation did he send to the giant king, Grim of Grimslott. The giant, however, made up his mind to attend the wedding feast, invited or not.

So now it is the wedding day. The mountain giant puts on his Dulde Hat and sets out with all his giant companions for the wedding feast. Only his wife is left at home to watch the castle.

The wedding guests are seated at the table. Great platters of food and pitchers of drink are brought in. But to the astonishment of the guests, both food and drink seem to vanish into thin air the moment they are set upon the table.

The farmer and his guests cannot understand what is happening. But one young lad thinks he knows who is at the bottom of this. So he slips away from the table, jumps on his horse, and rides straightaway to Borgasa Mountain.

On the steps of the Castle Grimslott stands the

giant's wife. She asks the lad how things are going at the wedding feast.

"The food is salt and the oil is sour," answers the lad. "That stingy farmer has hidden the wine and meat in the cellar where no one can find it. Now your husband sends greetings and he asks you to give me the Halde Hat so that he can find where the food is hidden."

The giant's wife suspects nothing. She gives the lad the Halde Hat, whereupon he hurries back to the wedding feast. As he enters the hall, he puts on the magic hat. At once he sees the giant king and his companions among the guests. They are grabbing all the food and all the drink the moment it is put upon the table.

The lad draws his sword and tells the other wedding guests to do the same.

"Stab as I stab, and cut as I cut!" he cries. And he begins to slash at the giants with his sword. The other guests follow his example, and they slay the giant king and all his companions.

From that time to this, so says the story, the castle upon Borgasa Mountain stands empty; and the people of Grimland are troubled no more by mountain giants.

—Adapted from a Swedish folk tale

A Legend of Knockmany
An Irish Comedy

Cast of characters:

    Fin M'Coul, a giant
    Oonagh, a giantess—Fin's wife
    Cucullin, a giant

    There are stories in this book about boys who fool giants and about giants who trick gods. But what happens when a giant—or rather, a giantess—tries to outwit another giant?

What Irish man, woman, or child has not heard of our renowned Hibernian Hercules, the great and glorious Fin M'Coul? Not one, from Cape Clear to the Giant's Causeway, nor from that back again to Cape Clear.

And, by the way, speaking of the Giant's Causeway brings me at once to the beginning of my story. Well, it so happened that Fin and his men were all working at the Causeway, in order to make a bridge across to Scotland. Suddenly Fin, who was very fond of his wife Oonagh, took it into his head that he would go home and see how the poor woman got on in his absence.

So, accordingly, he pulled up a fir tree and lopped off the roots and branches to make a walking stick of it. Then he set out on his way to Oonagh.

Now the truth is, that honest Fin's affection for his wife was by no manner of means the real cause of his journey home. There was at that time another giant, named Cucullin—some say he was Irish, and some say he was Scotch—but whether Scotch or Irish, sorrow doubt of it but he was a *targer*. No other giant of the day could stand before him. And such was his strength that, when well vexed, he could give a stamp that shook the country about him. The fame and name of him went far and near. And nothing in the shape of a man, it was said, had any chance with him in a fight.

The report went that, by one blow of his fists, he flattened a thunderbolt and kept it in his pocket, in the shape of a pancake, to show to all his enemies when they were about to fight him.

He had given every giant in Ireland a considerable beating, excepting Fin M'Coul himself. And he swore that he would never rest, night or day, winter or summer, till he would serve Fin with the same sauce—if he could catch him.

Fin, however, had a strong disinclination to meet a giant who could make an earthquake, or flatten a thunderbolt when he was angry. So he accordingly kept dodging about from place to place whenever he happened to get the hard word that Cucullin was on the scent of him. And now that he heard Cucullin was coming to the Causeway to a have a trial of strength with him, he was seized, in consequence, with a sudden fit of affection for his wife. He accordingly pulled up the fir tree as I said before and, having *snedded* it into a walking stick, set out on his travels to see his darling Oonagh.

111

Oonagh, or rather, Fin, lived at this time on the very tiptop of Knockmany Hill. In truth, the people wondered very much why it was that Fin selected such a windy spot for his dwelling house. The real state of the case was that he pitched upon the top of Knockmany in order that he might be able to see Cucullin coming toward the house.

"God save all here!" said Fin good-humoredly, on putting his honest face into his own door.

"Musha, Fin, avick, an' you're welcome home to your own Oonagh, you darlin' bully." Here followed a smack that is said to have made the waters of the lake at the bottom of the hill curl, as it were, in kindness and sympathy.

"An' what brought you home so soon, Fin?" said Oonagh.

"Why, avourneen," said Fin, putting in his answer in the proper way, "never the thing but the purest of love and affection for yourself. Sure you know that's truth, anyhow, Oonagh."

Fin spent two or three happy days with Oonagh and felt himself very comfortable, considering the dread he had of Cucullin. This, however, grew upon him so much that his wife could not but perceive something lay on his mind which he kept altogether to himself. Let a woman alone, in the meantime, for ferreting or wheedling a secret out of her good man when she wishes. Fin was a proof of this.

"It's this Cucullin," said he, "that's troubling me. When the fellow gets angry and begins to stamp, he'll shake you a whole townland. And it's well known that he can stop a thunderbolt, for he always carries one about him in the shape of a pancake, to show to anyone that might misdoubt it."

As he spoke, he clapped his thumb in his mouth, which he always did when he wanted to prophesy, or to know anything that happened in his absence.

"He's coming!" said Fin. "I see him below Dungannon."

"Thank goodness, dear! An' who is it, avick? Glory be to God!"

"That baste, Cucullin," replied Fin. "And how to manage I don't know. If I run away, I am disgraced. And I know that sooner or later I must meet him, for my thumb tells me so."

"When will he be here?" said she.

"Tomorrow, about two o'clock," replied Fin with a groan. "Oonagh, can you do nothing for me? Where's all your invention? Am I to be skivered like a rabbit

113

before your eyes, and to have my name disgraced forever in the sight of all my tribe, and me the best man among them? How am I to fight this man-mountain—this huge cross between an earthquake and a thunderbolt—with a pancake in his pocket that was once—"

"Be easy, Fin," replied Oonagh. "Troth, I'm ashamed of you. Talking of pancakes, maybe we'll give him as good as any he brings with him—thunderbolt or otherwise. If I don't treat him to as smart feeding as he's got this many a day, never trust Oonagh again. Leave him to me, and do just as I bid you."

This relieved Fin very much. For, after all, he had great confidence in his wife, knowing as he did that she had got him out of many a quandary before. The present, however, was the greatest of all.

Oonagh then drew the nine woolen threads of different colors, which she always did to find out the best way of succeeding in anything of importance. She then platted them into three plats with three colors in each, putting one on her right arm, one round her heart, and the third round her right ankle; for then she knew that nothing could fail with her that she undertook.

Having everything now prepared, she sent round to the neighbors and borrowed one-and-twenty iron griddles which she took and kneaded into the hearts of one-and-twenty round flat cakes of bread. These she baked on the fire in the usual way, setting them aside in the cupboard according as they were done.

She then put down a large pot of new milk which she made into pot cheese and gave Fin due instructions how to use the cheese when Cucullin should come. Having done all this, she sat down quite contented, waiting for his arrival on the next day about two o'clock, that being the hour when he was expected—for Fin knew as much by the sucking of his thumb.

Now this was a curious property that Fin's thumb had. In this very thing, moreover, he was very much resembled by his great foe Cucullin. For it was well known that the huge strength Cucullin possessed all lay in the middle finger of his right hand. And if he happened by any mischance to lose it, he would be no more, for all his bigness, than a common man.

At length, the next day Cucullin was seen coming across the valley, and Oonagh knew that it was time to commence operations. She immediately prepared the cradle and told Fin to lie down in it and cover himself up with the clothes.

"You must pass for your own child," said she. "So

115

just lie there snug, and say nothing, but be guided by me."

About two o'clock, as he had been expected, Cucullin came in. "God save all here!" said he. "Is this where the great Fin M'Coul lives?"

"Indeed it is, honest man," replied Oonagh. "God save you kindly—won't you be sitting?"

"Thank you, ma'am," says he, sitting down. "You're Mrs. M'Coul, I suppose?"

"I am," said she. "And I have no reason, I hope, to be ashamed of my husband."

"No," said the other, "he has the name of being the strongest and bravest man in Ireland. But for all that, there's a man not far from you that's very desirous of taking a shake with him. Is he at home?"

"Why, then, no," she replied. "And if ever a man left his house in a fury, he did. It appears that someone told him of a big basthoon of a giant called Cucullin being down at the Causeway to look for him. Troth, I hope for the poor giant's sake he won't meet him, for if he does, my Fin will make paste of him at once."

"Well," said the other, "I am Cucullin, and I have been seeking him these twelve months. I will never rest night or day till I lay my hands on him."

116

At this Oonagh set up a loud laugh of great contempt, and looked at him as if he were only a mere handful of a man.

"Did you ever see Fin?" said she.

"How could I?" said he. "He always took care to
keep his distance."

"I thought so," she replied. "I judged as much.
And if you take my advice, you poor looking creature,
you'll pray night and day that you may never see him.
For I tell you, it will be a black day for you when you do.
But, in the meantime, the wind's on the door, and as Fin
himself is from home, maybe you'd be civil enough to
turn the house, for it's always what Fin does when he's
here."

This was a startler even to Cucullin. He got up, however, and after pulling the middle finger of his right hand
until it cracked three times, he went outside, and getting his arms about the house, completely turned it as
she had wished. When Fin saw this, he felt the sweat of
fear oozing out through every pore of his skin. But
Oonagh, depending upon her woman's wit, felt not a
whit daunted.

"Arrah, then," said she, "as you are so civil, maybe
you'd do another obliging turn for us, as Fin's not here

to do it himself. You see, after this long stretch of dry weather we've had, we feel very badly off for want of water. Now, Fin says there's a fine spring well somewhere under the rocks behind the hill here below, and it was his intention to pull them asunder. But having heard of you, he left the place in such a fury that he never thought of it. Now, if you try to find it, troth, I'd feel it a kindness."

She then brought Cucullin down to see the place, which was then all one solid rock. After looking at it for some time, Cucullin cracked his right middle finger nine times and, stooping down, tore a cleft about four hundred feet deep and a quarter of a mile in length, which has since been christened by the name of Lumford's Glen.

"You'll now come in," said Oonagh, "and eat a bit of such humble fare as we can give you. Fin, even though he and you are enemies, would scorn not to treat you kindly in his own house."

She accordingly brought him in, and placing half a dozen of the cakes of bread we spoke of before him, together with a can or two of butter, a side of boiled bacon, and a stack of cabbage, she desired him to help himself.

Cucullin put one of the cakes of bread in his mouth

119

to take a huge whack out of it. "Blood and fury!" he shouted. "What kind of bread is this you gave me?"

"What's the matter?" said Oonagh coolly.

"Matter!" shouted the other again. "Why, here are the two best teeth in my head gone."

"Why," said she, "that's Fin's bread—the only bread he ever eats when at home. But indeed, I forgot to tell you that nobody can eat it but himself and that child in the cradle there. I thought, however, that, as you were reported to be rather a stout little fellow for your size, you might be able to manage it. And I did not wish to affront a man that thinks himself able to fight Fin. Here's another cake—maybe it is not so hard as that."

Cucullin at the moment was not only hungry, but ravenous, so he accordingly made a fresh set at the second cake, and immediately another yell was heard, twice as loud as the first. "Thunder and giblets!" he roared. "Take your bread out of this or I will not have a tooth in my head. There's another pair of them gone!"

"Well," replied Oonagh, "if you're not able to eat the bread, say so quietly and don't be wakening the child in the cradle there. There now, he's awake upon me."

Fin now gave a cry that startled the giant, as coming

from such a youngster as he was represented to be. "Mother," said Fin, "I'm hungry! Get me something to eat."

Oonagh went over, and put into his hand a cake that had no griddle in it. Fin soon swallowed it. Cucullin was thunderstruck, and secretly thanked his stars that he had the good fortune to miss meeting Fin. For, as he said to himself, "I'd have no chance with a man who could eat such bread as that, which even his son that's but in his cradle can munch before my eyes."

"I'd like to take a glimpse at the lad in the cradle," said he to Oonagh, "for I can tell you that the infant who can manage that nutriment is no joke to look at."

"With all the veins of my heart," replied Oonagh. "Get up, acushla, and show this decent little man something that won't be unworthy of your father, Fin M'Coul."

Fin, who was dressed for the occasion as much like a baby as possible, got up, and bringing Cucullin out, "Are you strong?" said he.

"Thunder an' ounds!" exclaimed the other. "What a voice in so small a chap!"

"Are you strong?" said Fin again. "Are you able to squeeze water out of this white stone?" he asked, put-

121

ting a stone into Cucullin's hand. Cucullin squeezed and squeezed the stone, but to no purpose. He might pull the rock of Lumford's Glen asunder, and flatten a thunderbolt, but to squeeze water out of a white stone was beyond his strength. Fin eyed him with great contempt as he kept straining and squeezing and squeezing and straining till he got black in the face with the effort.

"Ah, you're a poor creature!" said Fin. "You a giant! Give me the stone here, and when I show what Fin's little son can do, you may then judge of what my daddy himself is."

Fin then took the stone and slyly exchanged it for the pot cheese, which looked just like the white stone. Then he squeezed the cheese until the whey, as clear as water, oozed out in a little shower from his hand.

"I'll now go in," said he, "to my cradle. For I scorn to lose my time with anyone that's not able to eat my daddy's bread, or squeeze water out of a stone. Bedad, you had better be off out of this before he comes back. For if he catches you, it's in flummery he'd have you in two minutes."

Cucullin, seeing what he had seen, was of the same opinion himself. His knees knocked together with the terror of Fin's return, and he accordingly hastened in to bid Oonagh farewell, and to assure her that from that day out he never wished to hear of, much less to see, her husband. "I admit fairly that I'm not a match for him," said he, "strong as I am. Tell him I will avoid him as I would the plague, and that I will make myself scarce in this part of the country while I live."

"It's well for you," said Oonagh, "that Fin doesn't happen to be here, for it's nothing but hawk's meat he'd make of you."

"I know that," says Cucullin. "Divil a thing else he'd make of me. But before I go, will you let me feel what kind of teeth they are that can eat griddle-bread like that?"—and he pointed to it as he spoke.

"With all pleasures in life," said she. "Only, as they're far back in his head, you must put your finger a good way in."

Cucullin was surprised to find such a powerful set of grinders in one so young. But he was still more surprised on finding, when he took his hand from Fin's mouth, that he had left the very finger upon which his whole strength depended behind him. He gave one loud groan, and fell down at once with terror and weakness. This was all Fin wanted. He now knew that his most powerful and bitterest enemy was at his mercy. He

123

started out of the cradle, and in a few minutes the great Cucullin, that was for so long the terror of him and all his followers, lay a corpse before him.

Thus did Fin, through the wit and invention of Oonagh, his wife, succeed in overcoming his enemy by trickery, which he never could have done by force. And thus also is it proved that the women, if they bring us into many an unpleasant scrape, can sometimes succeed in getting us out of others that are as bad.

—William Carleton (abridged)

Big Giants and Tall Tales

The Giant

There is a Giant in the world
    Whose head is up so high,
He has to get down on his knees
    To look up in the sky.

And when he feels the need of food,
    He wades out to the sea
And fishes out a whale or two
    Just right to fricassee.

And when he tires of earthly food
    His diet, as a rule,
Consists of planets roasted well
    And hung outside to cool.

He sends his wife to gather them.
    She brings them on a tray.
For cream to make the planet sauce,
    She skims the Milky Way.

Whenever Mrs. Giant goes
    To tidy up the room,
She picks a comet, 'cause its tail
    Is handy for a broom.

The Giant dresses up sometimes
    And goes to take a stroll,
And picks a little bunch of stars
    To deck his buttonhole.

He puts a forest in his pipe
    When he's inclined to smoke,
And lights his match upon the moon—
    The moon can't see the joke!

The islands are his stepping stones,
    The continents his bed.
He slept on Greenland once and caught
    A snuffle in his head.

128

The Giant

He slides around the Arctic Pole.
    And if he gets a chill,
He goes and sits a month or two
    In India or Brazil.

He caught his trousers on Cape Horn,
    And tore an awful slit.
He stayed in bed a season while
    His wife embroidered it.
She fixed it with a patch of sky—
    It didn't show a bit!

When walking through a mountain land
    He sometimes stubs his toe.
The shock is called an earthquake by
    The frightened folks below.

One night a great astronomer
    While gazing into space,
By chance looked through his telescope
    Right in the Giant's face.

THE GIANT BOOK

He thought it was the moon until
    The Giant winked his eye.
The wise man never dared again
    To search the starry sky.

We never see the Giant for,
    On seeing us he flies
Because he feels so ill at ease
    And conscious of his size.

—Albert William Smith

130

The Giant who Rode
on the Ark

Long ago—I'm not sure how long, but it must have been hundreds and hundreds of years ago—people began to tell stories about the giants who lived in Noah's time, before the flood.

And they told about one giant in particular—a giant named Og, King of Bashan. It seems he was the greatest of all the giants. Just to give you some idea of how big Og was, here is what people used to say about him.

131

One day Og's tooth fell out. It was one of his baby teeth, so Og just threw it on the ground and forgot about it. Then Noah and his sons came along, and found Og's tooth. And they carved a bed out of it—a great ivory bed for Noah and his wife.

Og himself slept on an iron bed and sat on an iron chair. Only iron was strong enough to hold such a giant.

And to give you some idea how strong Og was—well, they say that just for fun Og would pull up a mountain and carry it on his head. And sometimes Og and his brother Sihon would play catch with a hill, tossing it back and forth as though it were a big ball.

After a game like that, Og would be so hungry and so thirsty that he would eat a thousand oxen at a sitting. And he would drink a thousand mugs of goat's milk. His brother Sihon would eat and drink almost as much.

As you can imagine, giants so big and so strong were afraid of nothing. When Noah told the giants to get ready for the flood, the giants laughed at him. "If all the waters of the earth be gathered together," boasted Og and his friends, "they will only reach up to our middles."

And then the rains came, and the waters rose and covered the earth. The valleys and the hills were covered by the waters. And Og and the other giants jumped from mountain to mountain because they did not want to get their feet wet. And still it rained, and the waters rose higher and covered the mountains—even the tops of the highest mountains.

So now the giants tried to stop the flood. They tried to stamp down the fountains of the great deep. And they tried to stop the windows of heaven with their hands. But the waters became boiling hot, and all the giants died. That is, all the giants died but Og, King of Bashan, who was a bit more clever than the others.

Now Og saw a huge animal behind the ark. It was the great reëm, a kind of giant rhinocerous. There was no room in the ark for the reëm, whose neck alone was three miles long. So Noah had tied the reëm to the ark by its single horn.

If, Og reasoned, the reëm can swim so happily alongside the ark, the water there cannot be boiling hot. And Og went into the water near the reëm. There the water was cool so that Og, too, could swim alongside the ark.

But after a while, Og grew tired, so he climbed on top of the ark. And he became hungry, so he struck a bargain with Noah.

"Let me ride on the ark, and give me food to eat," Og said to Noah, "and ever after I will be your servant.

I will serve you and your sons and your son's sons so long as I live."

Noah agreed and he cut a hole in the roof. And through the hole he doled out food to the giant Og. So the giant had a merry ride while Noah and his wife and his sons worked hard. For the day animals had to be fed by day. And the night animals had to be fed by night. And Og, King of Bashan, had to be fed day and night.

At last the rains stopped, and slowly the waters returned from off the earth. As soon as he saw the mountains appear above the waters, Og jumped off the ark and stood upon the mountain top.

And that, according to the ancient tales, is how, of all the giants, Og was the only one to be saved from the flood.

—adapted from Jewish legend

PEOPLE WHO BELIEVED IN GIANTS USED TO SAY—

MIST OR FOG RISING FROM A MOUNTAIN—is the smoke from a giant's pipe.

134

There was an old man of Coblenz
The length of whose legs was immense;
He went with one prance,
From Turkey to France,
That surprising Old Man of Coblenz.

      —Edward Lear

135

Gulliver in the Giants' Country

Most giant stories are so old that we don't know who first made them up. This story is different. It was published in England in 1726 (about fifty years before the American Revolution). That may seem old to you, but compared to other tales of giants, it isn't old at all. And we know exactly who wrote this story. His name is Jonathan Swift. The story comes from his book called *Travels into Several Remote Nations of the World by Lemuel Gulliver.*

Most of you have read about Gulliver's travels in Lilliput. (Gulliver looked like a giant to the tiny Lilliputians who were only five or six inches high.) But did you know that Gulliver also visited seven other countries, including Brobdingnag, the country of giants? To those giants, Gulliver was like a little toy, only six inches high.

Here is the story of some of Gulliver's astonishing adventures among the giants—almost exactly as Swift wrote it.

In June, 1702, I, Lemuel Gulliver, ship's surgeon, went on board the merchant-vessel *Adventure* bound for Surat. Rounding the Cape of Good Hope, we had a good voyage through the Straits of Madagascar. But just south of the equator a violent gale sprang up, and continuing for twenty days, drove us before it a little to the east of the Spice Islands.

Suddenly, the wind dropped and there was a perfect calm. I was delighted, but the captain, who knew those seas, bade us all prepare for a storm. The next day, just as he had said, a wind called the Southern Monsoon set in. We reefed the best we could, but it was a very fierce storm, and the waves broke strange and dangerous. We let our topmast stand, and the ship scudded before the sea.

Thus we were carried about five hundred leagues to the east, so that the oldest sailor aboard could not tell in what part of the world we were. Our provisions held out well, our ship was stanch, and our crew all in good health, but we were in great distress for lack of water.

The wind moderated, and the next day a boy on the topmast discovered land. Soon, we were in full view of an island or continent, on the south side of which was a neck of land jutting out into the sea, and a creek too shallow to hold our ship. We cast anchor about a league away, and our captain sent a dozen of his men well armed, in the longboat, with buckets for water. I asked his leave to go with them, to see the country and make what discoveries I could.

When we came to land, we saw no river or spring, nor any sign of inhabitants. Our men wandered on the shore, hoping to find some fresh water near the sea, and I walked alone on the other side where the country was all barren and rocky. Beginning to be tired, I started back toward the shore, only to see our men already in the boat rowing for dear life to the ship.

I was going to holloa to them when I saw a huge creature walking after them in the sea. The water was hardly to his knees, and he took prodigious strides. But our men had the start of him by half a league, and as the sea thereabout is full of sharp-pointed rocks, the monster was not able to overtake the boat. This I was told afterward, for I dared not stay to see, but ran as fast as I could the way I first went, and climbed up a steep hill which gave me a view of the country. I found it fully cultivated; but what first surprised me was the length of the grass, which in the hayfields was about twenty feet high.

I came upon a high road, for so I took it to be, though it served the inhabitants only as a footpath through a field of barley. Here I walked for an hour but could see little, for the grain rose forty feet into the air on either side. Coming at last to the end of the field, I found it fenced in with a hedge over one hundred feet high, and a stile impossible for me to climb.

I was trying to find a gap in the hedge when I saw a man as tall as a church steeple approaching the stile. Hiding myself in the grain, I heard him call, but the noise was so high in the air that at first I thought it was thunder. Immediately seven monsters, each with a reaping-hook as big as six scythes, came to reap the grain in the field where I was.

The next moment I saw an immense foot not ten yards away and the blinding gleam of a great reaping hook above my head. I screamed as loud as fear could make me. The huge reaper stopped short, and looking about on the ground for some time, finally spied me. He considered a while as if he were planning how he could pick up a small, dangerous animal so that it could neither bite nor scratch him. At last he ventured to take me up by the middle, between his forefinger and thumb, and held me within three yards of his eyes.

I resolved not to struggle as he held me in the air, about sixty feet from the ground, although he grievously pinched my sides. Instead, I raised my eyes and clasped my hands, speaking some words in a humble tone and groaning to let him know how cruelly I was hurt by the pressure of his thumb and finger. He seemed to understand, for putting me gently into his pocket, he ran along with me to his master, the farmer I had first seen.

The farmer blew my hair aside to get a better view of my face, and then placed me softly on the ground on all fours. But I got immediately up, and walked slowly backward and forward. Pulling off my hat, I made a low bow to the farmer. I fell on my knees, and spoke several words as loud as I could.

He spoke to me, but the sound of his voice pierced my ears like that of a water mill. I answered as loud as I could in several languages, and he laid his ear within two yards of me, but all in vain. We could not understand each other.

He then sent his servant to work, and taking out his handkerchief, spread it on his left hand, which he placed flat on the ground with the palm upwards. He beckoned

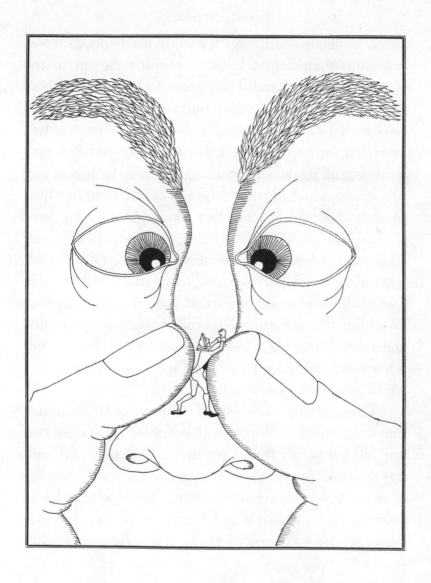

to me to step up on it, which I could easily do, as it was not more than a foot thick. Wrapping me up in the handkerchief, he carried me home to his house. There he showed me to his wife; but she screamed and ran back as if I had been a spider. However, when she had seen how gentle I was, and how well I obeyed the signs her husband made, she became extremely tender to me.

It was dinner time, and the servant brought in a dish of meat about twenty-four feet across. At the table were the farmer, his wife, and three children. The farmer placed me at some distance from him on the table, which was thirty feet high from the floor. I was in a terrible fright, and kept as far as I could from the edge, for fear of falling. The wife minced a bit of meat and crumbled some bread, placing it before me on a plate. I made her a low bow, took out my knife and fork, and began to eat, which gave them much delight.

Then the master beckoned me to come to his plate; but as I walked on the table, I stumbled against a crust and fell flat on my face. I got up immediately, and finding the good people greatly concerned, I waved my hat over my head, giving three *huzzas* to show that I had received no hurt. Just then I heard a noise like that of a dozen stocking-weavers at work, and turning my head, found it to be the purring of a cat three times as big as an ox. The fierce look of this creature, which had jumped into the mistress' lap, altogether discomposed me, although I stood at the further end of the table, fifty feet away.

But my chief danger came from another quarter. When dinner was almost over, a nurse came in with a child a year old in her arms, who immediately spied me and began a squall that you might have heard across London, to get me for a plaything. The mother put me towards the baby, who suddenly seized me by the middle, and put my head into his mouth, where I roared so loud that he was frightened and let me drop. And I should certainly have broken my neck if the nurse had not held her apron under me.

But the one of all the family whom I liked the best was a little girl nine years old, who became from the first my chief protector. It was she who fixed up a bed for me in her doll's cradle, and it was she who taught me the language. When I pointed out anything, she told me the name of it in the giants' tongue, so that in a few days I was able to call for whatever I wished. She was very good-natured, and not above forty feet high, being small for her age. She gave me the name of Grildrig,

143

meaning mannikin. I called her my Glumdalclitch, or little nurse.

It soon began to be known in the neighborhood that my master had found in the field a tiny animal shaped exactly like a human creature, which seemed to speak in a little language of its own, had already learned several words of theirs, walked erect on two legs, was tame and gentle, and would come when it was called. Another farmer, who lived near by, came on a visit on purpose to find out the truth of this story.

This man was thought to be a great miser, and to my way of thinking, he well deserved it, for the first thing he did after seeing me was to advise my master to show me as a sight in the next town.

Accordingly, the next market day, my master mounted his daughter, my little nurse, on a pillion behind him, and rode with me to town. I was carried in a wooden box, closed on every side, with a little door to let me in and out, and a few gimlet holes to give me air. Although Glumdalclitch had put her doll's quilt in the box for me to lie down on, I was nevertheless terribly shaken up by this journey of only half an hour. The horse went about forty feet at every step, and trotted so high that the motion was like the rising and falling of a ship in a great storm.

My master alighted at an inn; and having hired the crier to give notice of me through the town, placed me on a table in the largest room of the inn, which was about three hundred feet square. My little nurse stood on a low stool close by, to take care of me and direct what I should do. To prevent danger, my master would allow but thirty people at a time to see me, and set benches round the table so as to put me out of everybody's reach.

I walked about on the table as Glumdalclitch commanded; she asked me questions, and I answered them as loud as I could. I paid my humble respects to the audience, and said they were welcome. I took up a thimble filled with wine, and drank their health. I flourished my sword, and exercised with part of a straw as a pike. That day I was shown to twelve sets of people, and as often forced to go through the same antics till I was half-dead with weariness and vexation.

Finding how profitable I was, my master decided to take me to the metropolis. And so, having made my box more comfortable for a longer journey, he and Glumdalclitch set out with me for Lorbrulgrud, or the Pride of the Universe, three thousand miles away. Arriving there, my master hired a large room on the principal

145

street of the city, not far from the royal palace, and showed me ten times a day. The fame of me spread far and wide, for during the journey I had learned to speak the language fairly well, and understood every word I heard. Indeed, we had not been long in the city when a gentleman usher came from the palace, commanding my master to take me there immediately for the diversion of the queen and her ladies.

Her Majesty was beyond measure delighted with me. I fell on my knees, and begged the honor of kissing her imperial foot. But she ordered me to be set on a table, and held out her little finger toward me, which I embraced in both my arms, putting the tip of it with the utmost respect to my lips. She asked whether I would be content to live at court. I bowed down to the table, and answered that I should be proud to devote my life to Her Majesty's service. She then asked the farmer if he were willing to sell me at a good price. He said he would part with me for a thousand pieces of gold, which were ordered for him on the spot.

One request only I made of the queen: that Glum-dalclitch, who had always tended me with so much kindness, might continue to be my nurse and instructor. Her Majesty agreed, and easily got the farmer's consent. As

146

for the poor girl herself, she was not able to hide her joy.

The queen commanded her own cabinetmaker to make a box that might serve me as a bedroom. This man, who was most ingenious, in three weeks finished for me a wooden room, sixteen feet square and twelve high, with windows, a door, and two closets. The board that made the ceiling lifted up on hinges so that Glumdalclitch could take out my bed every day to air, and let it down at night, locking up the roof over me.

A skillful workman, who was famous for little curiosities, made me two tables and two chairs of a substance not unlike ivory. The room was quilted on all sides, as well as the floor and the ceiling, so that no harm might come to me if my box were carelessly carried, or jolted about in a coach.

The queen likewise ordered the thinnest silks that could be gotten to make me new clothes. But even these were thicker than blankets, and very much in my way till I was used to them.

So fond of my company did the queen become that she could not dine without me. I had a table placed on that at which she ate, just at her left elbow. Glumdalclitch stood on a stool near by, to assist and take care of me. I had an entire set of silver dishes, which in propor-

147

tion to the queen's were not much bigger than those of a doll's house.

After living among the giants several months, my first horror at their huge size so far wore off that I could not help smiling at myself when the queen used to place me on her hand before a mirror in which both our figures were reflected together. The contrast was so ridiculous that I really began to think I must have dwindled far below my usual size.

Indeed, I should have lived happily enough in Brobdingnag (for that is the name of the giants' country), if my littleness had not made me continually the victim of the most absurd accidents.

I remember one morning Glumdalclitch set me in my box on a window sill to give me the air. I opened my windows and sat down at my table to eat a piece of sweet-cake for breakfast, when twenty wasps as big as partridges came flying into the room, droning louder than so many bagpipes. Some of them seized my cake and carried it piecemeal away. Others flew about my head, deafening me with their noise, until I was afraid I should be stung to death. However, I had the courage to draw my sword, and attack them in the air. Four of them I killed, but the rest got away, and I shut my windows in a hurry.

Another day Glumdalclitch let me walk about by myself on a smooth grass plot in the garden, when there suddenly fell such a violent shower of hail that I was struck to the ground. And when I was down, the hailstones, which were as big as tennis balls, gave me such cruel bangs that I could scarcely creep to the shelter of a primrose. As it was, I was so bruised from head to foot that I could not go out for ten days.

But a more dangerous accident happened to me in the same garden when my little nurse had left me for a few minutes alone. While she was away, a small white spaniel belonging to one of the gardeners, ranged by the place where I lay. The dog, following the scent, came directly up, and took me in his mouth. Wagging his tail, he ran straight to his master, and set me gently on the ground.

Luckily, he had been so well taught, that I was carried between his teeth without the least hurt. But the poor gardener, who knew me well, was in a terrible fright. He took me up tenderly in both his hands, and asked me how I did; but I was so amazed and out of breath that I could not speak a word. In a few minutes, however, I came to myself, and he carried me safely to my little nurse.

The longer I stayed in Brobdingnag the fewer accidents I had, as I gradually adapted myself to the huge size of everything about me.

After a while, in fact, I even contrived a way so that I could read the giants' books, although they were several times as big as I was. The book I wished to read was opened and put leaning against the wall, and in front of it, a kind of stepladder, which the queen's carpenter had made for me, twenty-five feet high, and fifty wide. Mounting to the upper step of the ladder, I began reading at the top of the page, walking along to the right till I got to the end of the line. So I went, back and forth, till I had got a little below the level of my eyes. Then I descended gradually, going on in the same way to the bottom; after which I mounted again, and began the other page in the same manner. As for turning the leaf, that I could easily do with both hands, for it was as thick and stiff as pasteboard, and even in the largest books not more than twenty feet long.

But even though I was the favorite of a great queen and the delight of a whole court, I could not help sometimes wishing to be in a country where I need not live in fear of being stepped on like a toad or a young puppy.

150

But my escape came sooner than I expected, and in a most curious way.

Besides the large box in which I was usually carried, the queen had a smaller one made for me, about twelve feet square, for convenience in traveling. On top was a great ring, by which one of the giants could carry the box in his hand. And on one side were two iron loops, through which a person carrying me on horseback could run a leather belt and buckle it around his waist. The other sides had windows, latticed with iron wire to prevent accidents. Inside, I had a hammock swung from the ceiling, and a small hole cut in the roof just above it to give me air in hot weather. There were, besides, two chairs screwed to the floor so that they could not be tossed about by the motion of the horse or coach.

It was in this traveling box that I made my last trip in the giants' country. One spring I was carried in it to spend a few days at the seashore along with the queen and Glumdalclitch. My poor little nurse and I were tired by the journey. I had only a little cold, but Glumdalclitch was sick in bed. I longed to see the ocean, and asked leave to have one of the pages carry me along beside the sea. I shall never forget how unwillingly Glumdalclitch consented, bursting into a flood of tears, as if she had a foreboding of what was to happen.

The page took me out in my box, and walked with me on the rocks along the shore. Feeling slightly ill, I ordered him to set me down so that I could take a nap in my hammock. I got in, and the boy shut the window to keep out the cold. For some time I lay and watched him out the window, as he searched about among the rocks for birds' eggs. But after a while he went out of my sight altogether, and feeling more and more drowsy, I fell asleep.

There was a sudden violent pull on the ring of my box, and I awoke with a start. I felt my room raised high in the air, and then carried forward at a terrific speed. The first jolt almost shook me out of my hammock, but afterward the motion was easy enough. I called out several times as loud as I could, but all in vain. I looked out my windows, but could see nothing but clouds and sky. I listened, and made out a noise over my head like the flapping of wings. Then for the first time I realized what had happened. Some eagle had got the ring of my box in his beak. Soon, no doubt, he meant to let it fall on a rock like a turtle in a shell, and pick out my body to devour it.

Suddenly, the great wings above me began to beat

152

faster, and my box was tossed up and down like a swinging sign on a windy day. I heard several bangs, as I thought, given to the eagle and then felt myself falling straight down for more than a minute, but so swiftly that I almost lost my breath. My fall was stopped by a terrible squash that sounded louder to my ears than Niagara Falls; after which, I was in the dark for another minute. Then my box began to rise so high that I could see light from the tops of the windows. I now saw that my box had fallen into the sea, and with the weight of my body, the furniture, and the broad plates of iron on the bottom, floated about five feet deep in water.

I did then, and do still, suppose that the eagle which flew away with my box, was chased by two or three others who wanted a share in the prey. In defending himself he was forced to let me drop, but the iron plates on the bottom kept the box from breaking when it struck the water. Every joint was snugly fitted, and the door shut down, like a window, which kept my room so tight that very little water came in.

Nevertheless, I expected every minute to see my box dashed to pieces, or at least overturned by a wave. A break in a single pane of glass would mean immediate death, and indeed nothing could have saved the windows but the iron lattices the giants had put on the outside. I could not lift up my roof, or I should certainly have climbed out and sat on top, where I would at least have had a chance of living a few hours longer than by being shut up inside. But even if I escaped drowning for a day or two, what could I expect but a miserable death from cold and hunger?

After four hours of these wretched imaginings, I thought I heard a kind of grating noise on the side of my box where the iron loops were fixed. And soon after, I began to fancy that the box was being towed along in the sea, for now and then I felt a sort of tugging, which made the waves rise near the tops of my windows, leaving me almost in the dark. This somehow gave me a hope of escape, although I could not imagine how it could be brought about.

I unscrewed one of my chairs from the floor, and having managed to screw it down again directly under the air hole in the ceiling, I mounted on it and called for help in all the languages I knew. Then, fastening my handkerchief to my walking stick, I thrust it up through the hole, and waved it several times in the air, so that if any ship were near, the sailors might see that there was someone shut up in the box.

There was no reply to my signals, although I saw plainly that my box was moving along; and in an hour or so the side where the iron loops were, struck against something hard. I feared that it was a rock, for I was being tossed about more than ever. Suddenly, I heard a noise on the roof, like the grating of a cable passing through the ring, and I felt myself being hoisted up at least three feet higher than I was before. At that, I waved my stick and handkerchief again, and called for help till I was hoarse. In return I heard a great shout repeated three times. There was a trampling over my head, and a voice calling in English to ask if there was anybody below. I answered that I was an Englishman, and begged to be rescued from the prison I was in. The voice replied that I was safe, for my box was fastened to their ship, and the carpenter would come immediately to saw a hole in the roof large enough to pull me out. I said that was needless, for one of the crew had only to put his finger in the ring and take the box out of the sea into the ship.

On hearing me talk so wildly some of the crew thought I was crazy, and others laughed, for indeed it never occurred to me that now I was among people of my own height and strength. The carpenter came, and

in a few minutes sawed an opening about four feet
square, then let down a small ladder, which I mounted,
and from there took me to the ship.

The sailors crowded about me, asking me a thousand
questions, but I was all in a daze at the sight of so many
pigmies. For my eyes had been so long accustomed to
the giants that I could not believe these were ordinary-
sized Englishmen. However, the captain, seeing that I
was about to faint from weariness and amazement, took
me into his own cabin, and put me upon his own bed,
advising me to take a little rest.

I slept some hours, and when I woke up, felt much
better. It was then about eight o'clock at night, and the
captain entertained me most kindly at dinner. He said,
that about twelve o'clock at noon, as he was looking
through his glass, he spied my chest at a distance, and
thought it was a sail. As his ship's biscuit had begun to
run short, he made for it, hoping to buy some. On coming nearer and finding a huge chest instead of a ship,
he sent out his longboat to find out what it was. His men
came back in a terrible fright, swearing that they had
seen a swimming house.

Laughing at their folly, he went himself in the boat,
ordering his men to take a strong cable along with them.

156

He rowed around me several times, saw my windows, and the great iron loops upon the other side. To one of these loops he ordered his men to fasten a cable and tow the chest along toward the ship. When it was there he told them to fasten another cable to the ring in the cover, and raise the chest up with pulleys. But all the sailors tugging together were able to lift it only three feet. It was then they saw my stick and handkerchief waving through the hole, and decided that some unlucky man was shut up inside.

He asked me, how it was that I had come there, and I told him my story from beginning to end. And as truth always forces its way into reasonable minds, so this honest gentleman was not slow in believing me. He said he wondered at one thing very much, which was to hear me speak so loudly, and he asked whether either the king or queen of the giants was deaf. But I explained to him, how for the two years I had lived among the giants I had been like a man on the street talking to people in a steeple far above. I told him, too, how the sailors on the ship had seemed to me the tiniest little creatures I had ever seen, and how I almost laughed when I saw his table set for dinner, with plates the size of a penny, a leg of pork hardly a mouthful, and cups not so big as nutshells.

157

The captain laughed heartily, and during the whole voyage we were the best of friends. With a favorable breeze all the way, we rounded the Cape of Good Hope, and so sailed safely home to the tiny shores of England.

—adapted by Eunice Fuller

PEOPLE WHO BELIEVED IN GIANTS USED TO SAY—

A STRONG WIND—means a giant is blowing on his soup to cool it.

Paul Bunyan Swings His Axe

In America we seem to like things that are big. A giant in America is a hero—something to brag about. Tall stories about Paul Bunyan were first told by lumberjacks in the North Woods about a hundred years ago. Later, men came along and wrote down the stories. Here is a sample from the best book of Paul Bunyan stories I have ever read—*Paul Bunyan Swings His Axe* by Dell J. McCormick.

Many tales are told of Paul Bunyan the giant woodsman. Mightiest hero of the North Woods! A man of great size and strength who was taller than the trees of the forest. He had such strength in his huge arms that they say he could take the tallest pine tree and break it

159

in two with his bare hands. They tell of his mighty deeds and strange adventures from Maine to California.

A giant logger was Paul and he chopped down whole forests in a single day. His axe was as wide as a barn door and had a great oak tree for a handle. It took six full-grown men to lift it!

They say that he was born in Maine and even as a baby he was so large that his mother and father had to have fourteen cows to supply milk for his porridge.

Paul spent his boyhood in the woods and helped his father cut down trees.

Everybody liked young Paul, and for miles around they told of his great feats of strength: of how he took an iron crowbar and bent it into a safety pin to hold together a rip in his trousers; of how at another time he came to the end of the field he was plowing with two oxen and having no room to turn the plow and oxen around, picked up the plow, oxen and all, and turned them around to start back the other way.

Yet Paul never boasted. When people asked him how strong he was he just laughed. And when Paul laughed the folks in the villages ran into their houses and hid in the cellars, thinking it was a thunderstorm!

In spite of his huge size, Paul was as quick as lightning. They say he was the only man in the woods who could blow out a candle at night and hop into bed before it was dark.

Being so quick on his feet was once his undoing. He was out in the woods hunting one day and shot at a bear. Paul was anxious to see if he had hit, and ran lickety-split toward it, only to get there before the shot he had fired. The result was that he received a full load of his own buckshot in the seat of his breeches.

One day when Paul was working in his father's logging camp in the Maine woods it started to snow. Day after day the soft fluffy snowflakes fell until the entire camp was covered with a blanket of snow. Log cabins disappeared from sight, and all but the tallest trees were buried under the great snowdrifts.

And the strangest thing of all was that the snow, instead of being white, was a bright sapphire blue! For miles and miles, as far as one could see, the forest was covered with beautiful blue snow. Loggers even today remember that year and call it the Winter of the Blue Snow.

When the snow had stopped falling, Paul put on his snowshoes and went out to find wood for his fireplace. As he was returning, he noticed two little ears sticking up through a snowdrift.

"It must be some poor animal lost and freezing to death," thought Paul. He reached down with one of his great hands and scooped the little thing out of the snow. It was a baby ox calf with thin wobbly legs. Paul put the little calf inside one of his large pockets and took him home. Soon he was curled up in front of the fireplace and as happy and warm as could be.

"Poor little baby!" said Paul as the little calf drank some warm milk and gratefully caressed Paul's hand with his tongue. Paul decided to call the little calf "Babe" and to keep him for a pet.

The strangest thing about Babe was that, even after he became thawed out, his coat remained a soft glossy blue. Paul nursed his new pet back to health, but his color never changed. The Winter of the Blue Snow had colored him blue, and blue he remained forever after.

Babe followed Paul wherever he went and grew larger each day. Every time Paul looked around the little calf seemed to have grown a foot taller.

In the spring, Paul built a little barn for Babe and

put the calf inside for the night. The next morning, the barn was gone and so was the little blue calf. Paul searched high and low. Finally he found Babe calmly eating grass in a neighboring valley—with the barn perched right up on his back! He had outgrown it in a single night!

Paul became very fond of Babe and took him on all his adventures in the woods. He grew by leaps and bounds and soon was almost as large as Paul himself. Woodsmen tell us that when Babe was full grown he measured forty-two axe handles between the eyes.

His appetite was tremendous. Every evening he ate a ton and a half of hay. Even then he wouldn't be satisfied to go to bed unless he had three wagonloads of turnips for dessert.

Paul taught him to help with the logging in the woods, and would give him an eighty-pound lump of sugar if he had been a good ox during the day. Babe was always full of mischief, however. He liked to roar and stamp his feet at night so the men would run out of the bunkhouses where they slept, thinking it was an earthquake! When Paul scolded him for it, Babe only chuckled to himself and pretended he was asleep.

Once when Babe was standing beside the cookhouse

he winked at Paul and put his head in the cookhouse window. Babe gave a great sneeze and blew a whole barrel of flour over Hot Biscuit Slim, the cook, and his helper, Cream Puff Fatty!

Babe was very useful in many ways. For instance, Paul had a lot of trouble with the crooked, twisting road that wound in and out through the forest. He finally tied one end of the road to a large stump and hitched Babe to the other end with a large logging chain. Babe dug his great hoofs in the ground and strained and tugged until he had pulled the entire road out straight. It was a mighty feat of strength.

During his first summer, Babe became fat and lazy and one day refused to pull the logs down the road to the river. He wanted to wait until winter when the snow was on the ground and logs would slide easier. Paul didn't say a word, but that night he had the men secretly whitewash the road. The next morning, Babe thought it was snow and pulled the logs without further trouble.

When winter finally came again and covered the Maine woods with beautiful white snow, Babe was the happiest ox in the world. He loved to roam through the woods on the new snowshoes that Paul had given him for his first birthday.

In all the woods, there was no one so kind toward Babe as Paul Bunyan, and no ox was ever as faithful to its master as Babe, the famous Blue Ox.

One day Paul set out to build the largest logging camp in the world. People for miles around came to see it when it was finished. It was so big that when it was breakfast time in the kitchen, it was dinner time in the blacksmith shop at the other end of the camp. The dining room tables were two miles long, and the cookhouse boys wore roller skates so they could serve the food quickly.

It was a very busy camp.

As the trees fell, you could hear the men shouting, "Timber!! Timber-r-r!!" to warn the others.

Paul Bunyan finally invented the double-bitted axe with a blade on each side so his men could work twice as fast. Paul himself cut down the largest trees. Sometimes he chopped so fast his axe became red hot and had to be dipped into a lake of cold water every five minutes to cool it off.

Everything was on a huge scale in Paul Bunyan's camp.

The blacksmith, Ole the Swede, made a huge black kettle. It held eleven hundred gallons of soup.

When Hot Biscuit Slim made soup he rowed out into the center of the kettle with boatloads of cabbages, turnips, and potatoes, and shoveled them into the boiling hot water. In a few hours they had wonderful vegetable soup.

Next the blacksmith made a ten-acre griddle pan for hot cakes. Hot Biscuit Slim strapped flat sides of bacon on the feet of the cookhouse boys. They skated back and forth over the huge griddle until it was well greased.

Every Sunday morning for breakfast Paul's campers had hot griddlecakes. They were so large it took five men to eat one. Paul himself ate twelve or fourteen.

No one ever went hungry in Paul Bunyan's lumber camp.

When Paul Bunyan had cut down all the trees in North Dakota, he decided to go west. It was summertime, and the forest was sweet with the smell of green trees. The spreading branches cast their cool shadows on the ground.

"We must cross vast plains," said Paul to his men, "where it is so hot that not even a blade of grass can grow."

With Paul and Babe the Blue Ox leading the way, the men started across the plains on their long journey west. In a few days they had left the woods and were knee deep in sand that stretched out before them for miles and miles. The sun became hotter and hotter!

There was not a tree in sight. Paul Bunyan's men missed the cool shade of the trees. Whenever Paul stopped to rest, thirty or forty men would stand in his shadow to escape the boiling sun.

"I won't be able to last another day," cried Brimstone Bill, "if it doesn't begin to cool off soon!"

Even Paul Bunyan became tired finally and took his heavy double-bitted axe from his shoulder and dragged it behind him as he walked. The huge axe cut a ragged ditch through the sand that can be seen to this day. It is now called the Grand Canyon, and the Colorado River runs through it.

It became so hot that the men were exhausted and refused to go another step. Hot Biscuit Slim had complained that there was very little food left in camp. That night Paul took Babe the Blue Ox and went on alone into the mountains to the north. In the mountains Paul found a farmer with a barn full of corn.

"I will buy your corn," said Paul to the farmer. So he loaded all the corn on Babe's back and started for camp. By the time he arrived there, the sun was shining again and the day grew hotter as the sun rose overhead. Soon it became so hot that the corn started popping. It shot up into the air in vast clouds of white puffy popcorn.

It kept popping and popping and soon the air was filled with wonderful white popcorn. It came down all over the camp and almost covered the kitchen. The ground became white with popcorn as far as the eye could see. It fell like a snowstorm until everything was covered two feet deep with fluffy popcorn.

"A snowstorm! A snowstorm!" cried the men as they saw it falling. Never had they seen anything like it before. Some ran into the bunkhouses and put on their mittens and others put on heavy overcoats and woolen caps. They clapped each other on the back and laughed and shouted for joy.

"Let's make snowshoes!" cried Ole the Big Swede. So they all made snowshoes and waded around in the white popcorn and threw popcorn snowballs at each other, and everybody forgot how hot it had been the day

169

before.

Babe the Blue Ox knew it was only popcorn and winked at Paul.

Paul Bunyan chuckled to himself at the popcorn blizzard and decided to start west again while the men were feeling so happy. He found them all huddled around the kitchen fire.

"Now is the time to move on west," said Paul, "before it begins to get hot again." So they packed up and started. The men waded through the popcorn and blew on their hands to keep them warm.

After traveling for a few weeks more, they saw ahead of them the great forest they had set out to reach. They cheered Paul Bunyan who had led them safely over the hot desert plains. Babe the Blue Ox laughed and winked at Paul whenever anyone mentioned the great blizzard.

PEOPLE WHO BELIEVED IN GIANTS USED TO SAY—

EARTHQUAKES—happen when a giant sneezes so hard he shakes the earth.

Paul Bunyan

He came,
striding
over the mountain,
the moon slung on his back,
like a pack,
a great pine
stuck on his shoulder
swayed as he walked,
as he talked
to his blue ox
Babe;

171

a huge, looming shadow
of a man,
clad
in a mackinaw coat,
his logger's shirt
open at the throat
and the great mane of hair
matching,
meeting
the locks of night,
the smoke from his cauldron pipe
a cloud on the moon
and his laugh rolled through the mountains
like thunder on a summer night
while the lightning of his smile
split the heavens
asunder.

His blue ox, Babe,
pawed the ground
till the earth trembled
and shook
and a high cliff
toppled and fell;

172

Paul Bunyan

And Babe's bellow
was fellow
to the echo
of Bunyan's laughter;
and then
with one step
he was in the next valley
dragging the moon after,
the stars tangled,
spangled,
in the branches of the great pine.

—Arthur S. Bourinot

Giant Pears and
Giant Cows

In the olden times in the little country of Switzerland, things were different than they are today.

Take pears, for example. In the olden times Swiss pears were at least a thousand times bigger than the miserable fruit you see today.

You could really call those old-time pears Giant Pears.

Why, when an old-time Swiss pear fell from a tree, two men would come along with a crosscut saw to saw off the stem, load it onto a heavy oxcart, and drive it to the saw mill. There it would be cut into fine wooden panels—enough to panel a whole room.

The pear itself would be rolled along the ground and down into the cellar—and it took three strong men

174

to manage that. Once it was in the cellar, it was tapped and the juice drawn off—enough to make barrels and barrels of fine pear brandy.

Yes, things were different in little Switzerland in the olden times.

Take cows, for example. You could really call those old-time Swiss cows Giant Cows.

And the milk those cows gave! It was a problem to find a place to keep all that milk. Ponds had to be dug and the milk was squirted right into the ponds. Every day men used to row around the ponds in little boats, taking the cream off the top to make butter and cheese.

They say that one day a farmer sent around boats with propellers to whip the cream. He ended with a whipped cream mountain as high as the Alps. Well, that's what they say.

But one thing you can be sure of: those giant cows had gigantic horns. Now you know how the Swiss make blowing-horns out of cow's horns. Well, those giant cow's horns were so long that if you blew into one at Easter, the note didn't come out the other end till fifty days later, around Whitsuntide.

Things really were different in little Switzerland in the olden times.

175

How to Shake Hands with a Giant

(if you ever want to use your hand again)

Always carry an iron rod with you if you are in giant country. Then if you meet a giant who wants to shake hands with you, just hold out the iron rod.

If there is a fire handy, stick the rod in the fire first until it gets red hot. The giant will like that.

176

Permissions and Confessions

Courtesy demands, and publishers require, that I acknowledge the sources and indicate permissions granted for use of all copyrighted material included in this collection. I am happy to do so, and I am also glad to take this opportunity to indicate the sources of uncopyrighted material—for the benefit of other giant-hunters, or of anyone who is simply curious as to how this collection got collected.

First I must confess that I am unhappy at the thought of all the giants who are *not* in this book. No room. I must confess further, however, that I have purposely excluded modern giants created by individuals (except for Swift's Brobdingnagians). I wanted the strength of this collection to come from that powerful underground stream of tradition into which all storytellers and story-listeners must dip if their giant-lore is to have validity.

179

I have of course included the tried-and-true stories of Jack the Giant-killer and Jack and the Beanstalk. To omit them would be an act of snobbism. For me, a collection of giant stories without these two Jacks and their giants would be as disappointing as a zoo without monkeys.

My selections throughout the book are admittedly personal and partial. I simply immersed myself in giant lore and, by some mysterious, unfathomable force, certain stories were drawn to me—or was it I who was mysteriously, unfathomably drawn to certain stories? I know only that I love every story and verse in this book and that seems reason enough to include them.

Here are my acknowledgments and personal notes for each item:

JACK THE GIANT-KILLER

This story was assembled from several chapbooks dated 1815, 1842, and 1851. I have kept as close as possible to the language of the chapbooks. If this story sounds much like the Rackham version, it is because we have apparently both gone to the same sources.

HISTORY OF THE GIANTS

It is hard to decide which affords more delight—something astoundingly big or something amazingly small. So when a book listed in the library's card catalog as *History of the Giants* published in 1832 turned out to be a miniature book two and a half inches high, I wanted to share some of its pages with the readers of this collection. The additional verses, written in the same awkward vein as the ones in the book, are of course my own.

JACK AND THE BEANSTALK

Reprinted by permission of G. P. Putnam's Sons from *English Fairy Tales* by Joseph Jacobs. Mr. Jacob's telling has so much character and charm that I want to perpetuate it just as he wrote it—including the odd shifting of tenses at exciting moments. I share with Mr. Jacobs his scorn of the Victorian version of this story in which, to justify Jack's tricking the giant out of his treasures, a fairy is dragged into the story to explain that the treasure rightfully belongs to Jack because the giant had stolen it from Jack's father.

Jacobs usually refers to the giant as an ogre. I have taken the liberty of substituting the word giant throughout. I have also changed the last line of the Fee-fi-fo-fum formula from "I'll use his bones to grind my bread" to "I'll grind his bones to make my bread." (That's the formula as *I* remember it.)

PEOPLE WHO BELIEVED IN GIANTS USED TO SAY

Here are oddments culled from various sources. I must confess that the giant blowing on his soup is my own contribution to folklore. And why not? When collectors of oral tradition and folklore were going around the countryside in the nineteenth century interviewing peasants and other simple folk, I didn't happen to be around. If I had been, I'd have told the person interviewing me that a strong wind means a giant is blowing on his soup to cool it.

THE NINE-HEADED GIANT

From *Folk Tales from Korea* collected and translated by Zong-in-sob. With the permission of the publishers, Routledge & Kegan Paul Ltd. of London. I have rewritten and somewhat adapted this story from Mr. Zong's collection.

DAVID AND GOLIATH

I suppose I could have used one of the modern translations of the Bible, but I like the glory and the rhythm of the King James version.

THE THREE BROTHERS AND THE GIANT

I have freely translated and adapted this story from "*Les Trois Frères et le Géant,*" in *Litterature Orale de la*

182

Picardie, v. 13 of *Les Litteratures Populaires de Toutes les Nations*, edited by E. H. Carnoy, Paris, Maisonneuve, 1883.

GIUANNI AND THE GIANT

From *Italian Fables* by Italo Calvino © 1959 by the Orion Press, Inc., © 1956 by Giulio Einaudi editore S.p.A. Reprinted by permission of the Orion Press, Inc. I chose this story because I found it shorter and wittier and funnier than "Seven at One Blow" and other variants on this theme.

WHY ARE GIANTS SO STUPID?

Adapted from a fable in *Aesopi Fabulae* by E. Chambry. I used as the basis for my adaptation the French translation in the Budé series published in Paris in 1927. I must confess that the fable really seems to apply to tall men. I've stretched things a bit to apply it to giants.

ODYSSEUS IN THE LAND OF THE GIANTS

Reprinted with permission of the Macmillan Company from *The Children's Homer* by Padraic Colum, copyright 1918 by the Macmillan Company, 1946 by Padraic Colum and Willy Pogany. With the author's permission I have made minor changes and abridgements in this chapter.

THE CLEVER CAT AND THE GIANT

So far as I know, the statue of the cat exists only in my

183

own imagination. I have simply used the general motif (familiar to most readers from the story of *Puss in Boots*, but found in many other versions) as a basis for this anecdote.

THE GIANT WHO HAD NO HEART IN HIS BODY

I have used Sir George Dasent's translation of this Norse tale by P. C. Asbjornsen. Dasent introduced this celebrated Norwegian author to the English public in 1858.

THOR AND THE GIANTS

I have adapted the story from *Thor's Wonderful Journey* by Hamilton Wright Mabie. In order to focus on the dramatic contest between Thor and the giants, I have omitted the account of the journey. For the rest, I have made liberal use of the editor's pencil to lighten a rather murky syntax and to sharpen the story.

HALDE HAT AND DULDE HAT

I have adapted this story from a Swedish folk tale by Herman Hofberg who adds the following note: "The belief that giants have two hats, one of which renders the wearer invisible, and another that reveals things otherwise invisible, is widespread in northern Scandinavia."

A LEGEND OF KNOCKMANY

William Carleton (1794-1869) was intimately acquainted

with the Irish countryfolk whose tales he collected and re-fashioned. This legend, told by Carleton, has been shortened a bit and edited very lightly.

THE GIANT

These are only a few of the stanzas from the original verse by Albert William Smith which appeared in the *Ladies Home Journal*, and then in a collection of the author's non-sense verse published in 1910.

THE GIANT WHO RODE ON THE ARK

I must confess that I was really looking for a giant named Hurtali when I found Og. I was trying to trace the source of a children's story about a giant named Hurtali who rode on the ark. My only clue was a credit line reading "from an oriental tale." I failed to turn up Hurtali, but I did find that according to scattered references in the Midrash (exposition of Hebrew scriptures in which legends are often used to illustrate a point) it was Og, King of Bashan, who rode on the ark. My chief source for these Midrashic legends was *The Legends of the Jews,* a six-volume work by Louis Ginzberg.

I had, of course, to choose from various conflicting fragments. But I tried not to change the facts. It is true that nowhere is it said who actually slept in the ivory bed made of

185

Og's tooth. However, I like to think that Noah and his wife slept there. This is my small contribution to legend.

THERE WAS AN OLD MAN OF COBLENZ

This limerick can be found in any complete collection of Edward Lear's nonsense verse. The illustration is also Lear's.

GULLIVER IN THE GIANTS' COUNTRY

From *The Book of Friendly Giants* by Eunice Fuller. Copyright 1914 by the Century Company; renewed, 1942. Reprinted by permission of the publishers, Appleton-Century-Crofts, an affiliate of Meredith Press. Eunice Fuller has done a beautiful job of keeping Swift's style and at the same time making it more accessible to young readers. I have abridged her version slightly only because of lack of space.

PAUL BUNYAN SWINGS HIS AXE

From *Paul Bunyan Swings His Axe* by Dell J. McCormick, published by the Caxton Printers, Ltd., Caldwell, Idaho. Used by special permission of the copyright owner. Material from several chapters has been included to give readers a good sample of the fun in store for them when they read the entire book.

PAUL BUNYAN—poem

Canada has as much claim to Paul Bunyan as the U.S.A.

These are the first forty-seven lines of a poem by the Canadian poet Arthur S. Bourinot, and are published here with the permission of the author: "Paul Bunyan" is included in a collection of Bourinot's poems, *This Green Earth*, Carillon Poetry Chap-Books, 1953.

GIANT PEARS AND GIANT COWS

Freely adapted from "Giant Pear and Giant Cow," from *Swiss-Alpine Folk Tales*, by Fritz Müller-Guggenbühl, © Oxford University Press 1958. Adapted by permission.

Once again I must confess to being carried away by the spirit of folk-invention. This time I interpolated the bit about beating the lake of cream into Alps of whipped-cream.

HOW TO SHAKE HANDS WITH A GIANT

The idea for this useful "how-to" came from the following passage in "The Giant of Skalunda" in *Swedish Fairy Tales* by Herman Hofberg, translated by W. H. Meyers and published in this country in 1893:

"Where are you from?" inquired the giant . . .

"We are from Skalunda, if you wish to know," said one of the men.

"Give me your hand, for I wish to know if still there is warm blood in Sweden," said the giant.

187

The man, afraid of the grasp of the giant, drew a glowing iron rod from the fire, which he extended to the giant, who, grasping it with great force, squeezed it until the iron ran between his fingers.

"Ah, yes, there is still warm blood in Sweden," exclaimed he. . . .

THE BEST
MYSTERIES
OF ALL TIME

Mickey Spillane's stunning 1947 debut novel, *I, the Jury,* introduced the world to private eye Mike Hammer, one of the most popular and imitated series characters in crime fiction. The tough-talking detective set the standard for gutsy, hard-boiled crime fighters in books, film, and television. Although *I, the Jury*'s more violent moments shocked some critics in the staid 1950s, Spillane's straight-forward, fast-paced writing struck an immediate chord with readers. The author wrote more than two dozen novels, which have sold 130 million copies worldwide in the past half century—a rare feat for even the most acclaimed writers. Spillane received the Grand Master award from the Mystery Writers of America in 1995, and *I, the Jury,* is widely considered his most powerful story.

I, the Jury

ALSO BY MICKEY SPILLANE

The Big Kill

Bloody Sunrise

The Body Lovers

The By-Pass Control

The Day of the Guns

The Death Dealers

The Deep

The Delta Factor

The Girl Hunters

Killer Mine

Kiss Me, Deadly

The Long Wait

Me, Hood

My Gun Is Quick

One Lonely Night

The Snake

The Twisted Thing

The Tough Guys

Vengeance Is Mine

MICKEY SPILLANE

THE BEST
MYSTERIES
OF ALL TIME

ImPress • Pleasantville, New York

THE BEST MYSTERIES OF ALL TIME

I, THE JURY

ImPress is an imprint of The Reader's Digest Association, Inc.,
Bedford Road, Pleasantville, New York 10570.

ISSN 1544-4007

PRINTED IN THE UNITED STATES OF AMERICA

I, the Jury

chapter 1

I SHOOK the rain from my hat and walked into the room. Nobody said a word. They stepped back politely and I could feel their eyes on me. Pat Chambers was standing by the door to the bedroom trying to steady Myrna. The girl's body was racking with dry sobs. I walked over and put my arms around her.

"Take it easy, kid," I told her. "Come on over here and lie down." I led her to a studio couch that was against the far wall and sat her down. She was in pretty bad shape. One of the uniformed cops put a pillow down for her and she stretched out.

Pat motioned me over to him and pointed to the bedroom. "In there, Mike," he said.

In there. The words hit me hard. In there was my best friend lying on the floor dead. The body. Now I could call it that. Yesterday it was Jack Williams, the guy that shared the same mud bed with me through two years of warfare in the stinking slime of the jungle. Jack, the guy who said he'd give his right arm for a friend and did when he stopped a bastard of a Jap from slitting me in two. He caught the bayonet in the biceps and they amputated his arm.

Pat didn't say a word. He let me uncover the body and feel the cold face. For the first time in my life I felt like crying. "Where did he get it, Pat?"

"In the stomach. Better not look at it. The killer carved the nose off a forty-five and gave it to him low."

I threw back the sheet anyway and a curse caught in my throat. Jack was in shorts, his one hand still clutching his belly in agony. The bullet went in clean, but where it came out left a hole big enough to cram a fist into.

Very gently I pulled the sheet back and stood up. It wasn't a complicated setup. A trail of blood led from the table beside the bed to where Jack's artificial arm lay. Under him the throw rug was ruffled and twisted. He had tried to drag himself along with his one arm, but never reached what he was after.

His police positive, still in the holster, was looped over the back of the chair. That was what he wanted. With a slug in his gut he never gave up.

I pointed to the rocker, overbalanced under the weight of the .38. "Did you move the chair, Pat?"

"No, why?"

"It doesn't belong there. Don't you see?"

2

Pat looked puzzled. "What are you getting at?"

"That chair was over there by the bed. I've been here often enough to remember that much. After the killer shot Jack, he pulled himself toward the chair. But the killer didn't leave after the shooting. He stood here and watched him grovel on the floor in agony. Jack was after that gun, but he never reached it. He could have if the killer didn't move it. The trigger-happy bastard must have stood by the door laughing while Jack tried to make his last play. He kept pulling the chair back, inch by inch, until Jack gave up. Tormenting a guy who's been through all sorts of hell. Laughing. This was no ordinary murder, Pat. It's as cold-blooded and as deliberate as I ever saw one. I'm going to get the one that did this."

"You dealing yourself in, Mike?"

"I'm in. What did you expect?"

"You're going to have to go easy."

"Uh-uh. Fast, Pat. From now on it's a race. I want the killer for myself. We'll work together as usual, but in the homestretch, I'm going to pull the trigger."

"No, Mike, it can't be that way. You know it."

"Okay, Pat," I told him. "You have a job to do, but so have I. Jack was about the best friend I ever had. We lived together and fought together. And by Christ, I'm not letting the killer go through the tedious process of the law. You know what happens, damn it. They get the best lawyer there is and screw up the whole thing and wind up a hero! The dead can't speak for themselves. They can't tell what happened. How could Jack tell a jury what it was like to have his insides ripped out by a dumdum? Nobody in the box would know how it felt to be dying or have your own killer laugh in your face. One arm. Hell, what does that mean? So he has the Purple Heart. But did they ever try dragging themselves across a floor to a gun with that one arm, their insides filling up with blood, so goddamn mad to be shot they'd do anything to reach the killer. No, damn it. A jury is cold and impartial like they're supposed to be, while some snotty lawyer makes them pour tears as he tells how his client was insane at the moment or had to shoot in self-defense. Swell. The law is fine. But this time I'm the law and I'm not going to be cold and impartial. I'm going to remember all those things."

I reached out and grabbed the lapels of his coat. "And something more, Pat. I want you to hear every word I say. I want you to tell it to everyone you know. And when you tell it, tell it strong, because I mean every word of it. There arc ten thousand mugs that hate me and you know it. They hate me because if they mess with me I shoot their damn heads off. I've done it and I'll do it again."

There was so much hate welled up inside me I was ready to blow up, but I turned and looked down at what was once Jack. Right then I felt like saying a prayer, but I was too mad.

"Jack, you're dead now. You can't hear me any more. Maybe you can. I hope so. I want you to hear what I'm about to say. You've known me a long time, Jack. My word is good just as long as I live. I'm going to get the louse that killed you. He won't sit in the chair. He won't hang. He will die exactly as you died, with a .45 slug in the gut, just a little below the belly button. No matter who it is, Jack, I'll get the one. Remember, no matter who it is, I promise."

When I looked up, Pat was staring at me strangely. He shook his head. I knew what he was thinking. "Mike, lay off. For God's sake don't go off half-cocked about this. I know you too well. You'll start shooting up anyone connected with this and get in a jam you'll never get out of."

"I'm over it now, Pat. Don't get excited. From now on I'm after one thing, the killer. You're a cop, Pat. You're tied down by rules and regulations. There's someone over you. I'm alone. I can slap someone in the puss and they can't do a damn thing. No one can kick me out of my job. Maybe there's nobody to put up a huge fuss if I get gunned down, but then I still have a private cop's license with the privilege to pack a rod, and they're afraid of me. I hate hard, Pat. When I latch on to the one behind this they're going to wish they hadn't started it. Some day, before long, I'm going to have my rod in my mitt and the killer in front of me. I'm going to watch the killer's face. I'm going to plunk one right in his gut, and when he's dying on the floor I may kick his teeth out.

"You couldn't do that. You have to follow the book because you're a Captain of Homicide. Maybe the killer will wind up in the chair. You'd be satisfied, but I wouldn't. It's too easy. That killer is going down like Jack did."

There was nothing more to say. I could see by the set of Pat's jaw that he wasn't going to try to talk me out of it. All he could do was to try to beat me to him and take it from there. We walked out of the room together. The coroner's men had arrived and were ready to carry the body away.

I didn't want Myrna to see that. I sat down on the couch beside her and let her sob on my shoulder. That way I managed to shield her from the sight of her fiancé being carted off in a wicker basket. She was a good kid. Four years ago, when Jack was on the force, he had grabbed her as she was about to do a Dutch over the

Brooklyn Bridge. She was a wreck then. Dope had eaten her nerve ends raw. But he had taken her to his house and paid for a full treatment until she was normal. For the both of them it had been a love that blossomed into a beautiful thing. If it weren't for the war they would have been married long ago.

When Jack came back with one arm it had made no difference. He no longer was a cop, but his heart was with the force. She had loved him before and she still loved him. Jack wanted her to give up her job, but Myrna persuaded him to let her hold it until he really got settled. It was tough for a man with one arm to find employment, but he had many friends.

Before long he was part of the investigating staff of an insurance company. It had to be police work. For Jack there was nothing else. Then they were happy. Then they were going to be married. Now this.

Pat tapped me on the shoulder. "There's a car waiting downstairs to take her home."

I rose and took her by the hand. "Come on, kid. There's no more you can do. Let's go."

She didn't say a word, but stood up silently and let a cop steer her out the door. I turned to Pat. "Where do we start?" I asked him.

"Well, I'll give you as much as I know. See what you can add to it. You and Jack were great buddies. It might be that you can add something that will make some sense."

Inwardly I wondered. Jack was such a straight guy that he never made an enemy. Even while on the force. Since he'd gotten back, his work with the insurance company was pretty routine. But maybe an angle there, though.

"Jack threw a party last night," Pat went on. "Not much of an affair."

"I know," I cut in, "he called me and asked me over, but I was pretty well knocked out. I hit the sack early. Just a group of old friends he knew before the army."

"Yeah. We got their names from Myrna. The boys are checking on them now."

"Who found the body?" I asked.

"Myrna did. She and Jack were driving out to the country today to pick a building site for their cottage. She got here at eight a.m. or a little after. When Jack didn't answer, she got worried. His arm had been giving him trouble lately and she thought it might have been that. She called the super. He knew her and let her in. When she screamed the super came running back and called us. Right after I got the story about the party from her, she broke down completely. Then I called you."

"What time did the shooting occur?"

"The coroner places it about five hours before I got here. That would make it about three fifteen. When I get an autopsy report we may be able to narrow it down even further."

"Anyone hear a shot?"

"Nope. It probably was a silenced gun."

"Even with a muffler, a .45 makes a good-sized noise."

"I know, but there was a party going on down the hall. Not loud enough to cause complaints, but enough to cover up any racket that might have been made here."

"What about those that were here?" Pat reached in his pocket and pulled out a pad. He ripped a leaf loose and handed it to me.

"Here's a list Myrna gave me. She was the first to arrive. Got here at eight thirty last night. She acted as hostess, meeting the others at the door. The last one came about eleven. They spent the evening doing some light drinking and dancing, then left as a group about one."

I looked at the names Pat gave me. A few of them I knew well enough, while a couple of the others were people of whom Jack had spoken, but I had never met.

"Where did they go after the party, Pat?"

"They took two cars. The one Myrna went in belonged to Hal Kines. They drove straight up to Westchester, dropping Myrna off on the way. I haven't heard from any of the others yet."

Both of us were silent for a moment, then Pat asked, "What about a motive, Mike?"

I shook my head. "I don't see any yet. But I will. He wasn't killed for nothing. I'll bet this much, whatever it was, was big. There's a lot here that's screwy. You got anything?"

"Nothing more than I gave you, Mike. I was hoping you could supply some answers."

I grinned at him, but I wasn't trying to be funny. "Not yet. Not yet. They'll come though. And I'll relay them on to you, but by that time I'll be working on the next step."

"The cops aren't exactly dumb, you know. We can get our own answers."

"Not like I can. That's why you buzzed me so fast. You can figure things out as quickly as I can, but you haven't got the ways and means of doing the dirty work. That's where I come in. You'll be right behind me every inch of the way, but when the pinch comes I'll get shoved aside and you slap the cuffs on. That is, if you can shove me aside. I don't think you can."

"Okay, Mike, call it your own way. I want you in all right. But I want the killer, too. Don't forget that. I'll be trying to beat you to him. We have every scientific facility at our disposal and a lot of men to do the leg work. We're not short in brains, either," he reminded me.

"Don't worry, I don't underrate the cops. But cops can't break a guy's arm to make him talk, and they can't shove his teeth in with the muzzle of a .45 to remind him that you aren't fooling. I do my own leg work, and there are a lot of guys who will tell me what I want to know because they know what I'll do to them if they don't. My staff is strictly ex officio, but very practical."

That ended the conversation. We walked out into the hall where Pat put a patrolman on the door to make sure things stayed as they were. We took the self-operated elevator down four flights to the lobby and I waited while Pat gave a brief report to some reporters.

My car stood at the curb behind the squad car. I shook hands with Pat and climbed into my jalopy and headed for the Hackard Building, where I held down a two-room suite to use for operation.

chapter 2

THE office was locked when I got there. I kicked on the door a few times and Velda clicked the lock back. When she saw who it was she said, "Oh, it's you."

"What do you mean—'Oh, it's you'! Surely you remember me, Mike Hammer, your boss."

"Poo! You haven't been here in so long I can't tell you from another bill collector." I closed the door and followed her into my sanctum sanctorum. She had million-dollar legs, that girl, and she didn't mind showing them off. For a secretary she was an awful distraction. She kept her coal-black hair long in a page-boy cut and wore tight-fitting dresses that made me think of the curves in the Pennsylvania Highway every time I looked at her. Don't get the idea that she was easy, though. I've seen her give a few punks the brush off the hard way. When it came to quick action she could whip off a shoe and crack a skull before you could bat an eye.

Not only that, but she had a private op's ticket and on occasions when she went out with me on a case, packed a flat .32 automatic—and she wasn't afraid to use it. In the three years she worked for me I never made a pass at her. Not that I didn't want to, but it would be striking too close to home.

Velda picked up her pad and sat down. I plunked myself in the old swivel chair, then swung around facing the window. Velda threw a thick packet on my desk. "Here's all the information I could get on those that were at the party last night."

I looked at her sharply. "How did you know about Jack? Pat only called my home."

Velda wrinkled that pretty face of hers up into a cute grin. "You forget that I have an in with a few reporters. Tom Dugan from the *Chronicle* remembered that you and Jack had been good friends. He called here to see what he could get and wound up by giving me all the info he had—and I didn't have to sex him, either." She put that in as an afterthought. "Most of the gang at the party were listed in your files. Nothing sensational. I got a little data from Tom who had more personal dealings with a few of them. Mostly character studies and some society reports. Evidently they were people whom Jack had met in the past and liked. You've even spoken about several yourself."

I tore open the package and glanced at a sheaf of photos. "Who are these?"

Velda looked over my shoulder and pointed them out. "Top one is Hal Kines, a med student from a university upstate. He's about twenty-three, tall, and looks like a crew man. At least that's the way he cuts his hair." She flipped the page over. "These two are the Bellemy twins. Age, twenty-nine, unmarried. In the market for husbands. Live off the fatta the land with dough their father left them. A half interest in some textile mills someplace down South."

"Yeah," I cut in, "I know them. Good lookers, but not very bright. I met them at Jack's place once and again at a dinner party."

She pointed to the next one. A newspaper shot of a middle-aged guy with a broken nose. George Kalecki. I knew him pretty well. In the roaring twenties he was a bootlegger. He came out of the crash with a million dollars, paid up his income tax, and went society. He fooled a lot of people but he didn't fool me. He still had his finger in a lot of games just to keep in practice. Nothing you could pin on him though. He kept a staff of lawyers on their toes to keep him clean and they were doing a good job. "What about him?" I asked her.

"You know more than I do. Hal Kines is staying with him. They live about a mile above Myrna in Westchester." I nodded. I remembered Jack talking about him. He had met George through Hal. The kid had been a friend of George ever since the older man had met him through some mutual acquaintance. George was the guy that was putting him through college, but why, I wasn't sure.

The next shot was one of Myrna with a complete history of her that Jack had given me. Included was a medical record from the hospital when he had made her go cold turkey, which is dope-addict talk for an all-out cure. They cut them off from the stuff completely. It either kills them or cures them. In Myrna's case, she made it. But she made Jack promise that he would never try to get any information from her about where she got the stuff. The way he fell for the girl, he was ready to do anything she asked, and so far as he was concerned, the matter was completely dropped.

I flipped through the medical record. Name, Myrna Devlin. Attempted suicide while under the influence of heroin. Brought to emergency ward of General Hospital by Detective Jack Williams. Admitted 3-15-40. Treatment complete 9-21-40. No information available on patient's source of narcotics. Released into custody of Detective Jack Williams 9-30-40. Following this was a page of medical details which I skipped.

"Here's one you'll like, chum." Velda grinned at me. She pulled out a full-length photo of a gorgeous blonde. My heart jumped when I saw it. The picture was taken at a beach, and she stood there tall and languid-looking in a white bathing suit. Long solid legs. A little heavier than the movie experts consider good form, but the kind that make you drool to look at. Under the suit I could see the muscles of her stomach. Incredibly wide shoulders for a woman, framing breasts that jutted out, seeking freedom from the restraining fabric of the suit. Her hair looked white in the picture, but I could tell that it was a natural blonde. Lovely, lovely yellow hair. But her face was what got me. I thought Velda was a good looker, but this one was even lovelier. I felt like whistling.

"Who is she?"

"Maybe I shouldn't tell you. That leer on your face could get you into trouble, but it's all there. Name's Charlotte Manning.

She's a female psychiatrist with offices on Park Avenue, and very successful. I understand she caters to a pretty ritzy clientele."

I glanced at the number and made up my mind that right here was something that made this business a pleasurable one. I didn't say that to Velda. Maybe I'm being conceited, but I've always had the impression that she had designs on me. Of course she never mentioned it, but whenever I showed up late in the office with lipstick on my shirt collar, I couldn't get two words out of her for a week.

I stacked the sheaf back on my desk and swung around in the chair. Velda was leaning forward ready to take notes. "Want to add anything, Mike?"

"Don't think so. At least not now. There's too much to think about first. Nothing seems to make sense."

"Well, what about motive? Could Jack have had any enemies that caught up with him?"

"Nope. None I know of. He was square. He always gave a guy a break if he deserved it. Then, too, he never was wrapped up in anything big."

"Did he own anything of any importance?"

"Not a thing. The place was completely untouched. He had a few hundred dollars in his wallet that was lying on the dresser. The killing was done by a sadist. He tried to reach his gun, but the killer pulled the chair it hung on back slowly, making him crawl after it with a slug in his gut, trying to keep his insides from falling out with his hand."

"Mike, please."

I said no more. I just sat there and glowered at the wall. Some-day I'd trigger the bastard that shot Jack. In my time I've done it plenty of times. No sentiment. That went out with the first. After the war I've been almost anxious to get to some of the rats that make up the section of humanity that prey on people. People. How incredibly stupid they could be sometimes. A trial by law for a killer. A loophole in the phrasing that lets a killer crawl out. But in the end the people have their justice. They get it through guys like me once in a while. They crack down on society and I crack down on them. I shoot them like the mad dogs they are and society drags me to court to explain the whys and wherefores of the extermination. They investigate my past, check my fingerprints and throw a million questions my way. The papers make me look like a kill-crazy shamus, but they don't bear down too hard because Pat Chambers keeps them off my neck. Besides, I do my best to help the boys out and they know it. And I'm usually good for a story when I wind up a case.

Velda came back into the office with the afternoon edition of the sheets. The kill was spread all over the front page, followed by a four-column layout of what details were available. Velda was reading over my shoulder and I heard her gasp.

"Did you come in for a blasting! Look." She was pointing to the last paragraph. There was my tie-up with the case, but what she was referring to was the word-for-word statement that I had made to Jack. My promise. My word to a dead friend that I would kill this murderer as he had killed him. I rolled the paper into a ball and threw it viciously at the wall.

"That louse! I'll break his filthy neck for printing that. I meant what I said when I made that promise. It's sacred to me, and they make a joke out of it. Pat did that. And I thought he was a friend. Give me the phone."

Velda grabbed my arm. "Take it easy. Suppose he did. After all, Pat's still a cop. Maybe he saw a chance of throwing the killer your way. If the punk knows you're after him for keeps he's liable not to take it standing still and make a play for you. Then you'll have him."

"Thanks, kid," I told her, "but your mind's too clean. I think you got the first part right, but your guess on the last part smells. Pat doesn't want me to have any part of him because he knows the case is ended right there. If he can get the killer to me you can bet your grandmother's uplift bra that he'll have a tail on me all the way with someone ready to stop in when the shooting starts."

"I don't know about that, Mike. Pat knows you're too smart not to recognize when you're being tailed. I wouldn't think he'd do that."

"Oh, no? He isn't dumb by any means. I'll bet you a sandwich against a marriage license he's got a flatfoot downstairs covering every exit in the place ready to pick me up when I leave. Sure, I'll shake them, but it won't stop there. A couple of experts will take up where they leave off."

Velda's eyes were glowing like a couple of hot brands. "Are you serious about that? About the bet, I mean?"

I nodded. "Dead serious. Want to go downstairs with me and take a look?" She grinned and grabbed her coat. I pulled on my battered felt and we left the office, but not before I had taken a second glance at the office address of Charlotte Manning.

Pete, the elevator operator, gave me a toothy grin when we stepped into the car. "Evening, Mr. Hammer," he said.

I gave him an easy jab in the short ribs and said, "What's new with you?"

"Nothing much, 'cepting I don't get to sit down much on the job anymore." I had to grin. Velda had lost the bet already. That little piece of simple repartee between Pete and myself was a code system we had rigged up years ago. His answer meant that I was going to have company when I left the building. It cost me a fin a week but it was worth it. Pete could spot a flatfoot faster than I can. He should. He had been a pickpocket until a long stretch up the river gave him a turn of mind.

For a change I decided to use the front entrance. I looked around for my tail but there was none to be seen. For a split second my heart leaped into my throat. I was afraid Pete had gotten his signals crossed. Velda was a spotter, too, and the smile she was wearing as we crossed the empty lobby was a thing to see. She clamped onto my arm ready to march me to the nearest justice of the peace.

But when I went through the revolving doors her grin passed as fast as mine appeared. Our tail was walking in front of us. Velda said a word that nice girls don't usually use, and you see scratched in the cement by some evil-minded guttersnipe.

This one was smart. We never saw where he came from. He walked a lot faster than we did, swinging a newspaper from his hand against his leg. Probably, he spotted us through the windows behind the palm, then seeing what exit we were going to use, walked around the corner and came past us as we left. If we had gone the other way, undoubtedly there was another ready to pick us up.

But this one had forgotten to take his gun off his hip and stow it under his shoulder, and guns make a bump look the size of a pumpkin when you're used to looking for them.

When I reached the garage he was nowhere to be seen. There were a lot of doors he could have ducked behind. I didn't waste time looking for him. I backed the car out and Velda crawled in beside me. "Where to now?" she asked.

"The automat, where you're going to buy me a sandwich."

chapter 3

I DUMPED Velda at her hairdresser's after we ate, then headed north to Westchester. I hadn't planned to call on George Kalecki until the following day, but a call to Charlotte's office dealt that one out. She had left for home, and the wench in the reception room had been instructed not to give her address. I told her I'd call later and left a message that I wanted to see her as soon as possible. I couldn't get that woman off my mind. Those legs.

Twenty minutes later I was pulling the bell outside a house that must have cost a cool quarter million. A very formal butler clicked the lock and admitted me. "Mr. Kalecki," I said.

"Who shall I say is calling, sir?"

"Mike Hammer. I'm a private detective." I flashed my tin on him but he wasn't impressed.

"I'm rather afraid Mr. Kalecki is indisposed at the moment, sir," he told me. I recognized a pat standoff when I saw one, but I wasn't bothered.

"Well, you tell him to un-dispose himself right away and get his tail down here or I'll go get him. And I'm not kidding, either."

The butler looked me over carefully and must have decided that I meant what I said. He nodded and took my hat. "Right this way, Mr. Hammer." He led me to an oversize library and I plunked myself in an armchair and waited for George Kalecki.

He wasn't long coming. The door banged open and a grey-haired guy a little stouter than his picture revealed came in. He didn't waste words. "Why did you come in after my man informed you that I was not to be disturbed?"

I lit a butt and blew the smoke at him. "Don't give me that stuff, chum. You know why I'm here."

"No doubt. I read the papers. But I'm afraid that I can't help you. I was home in bed when the murder occurred and I can prove it."

"Hal Kines came in with you?"

"Yes."

"Did your servant let you in?"

"No, I used my own key."

"Did anyone else beside Hal see you come in?"

"I don't think so, but his word is good enough."

I sneered into his face. "Not when the both of you are possible murder suspects, it isn't."

Kalecki turned pale when I said that. His mouth worked a little and he looked ready to kill me. "How dare you say that," he snarled at me. "The police have not made an attempt to connect me with that killing. Jack Williams died hours after I left."

I took a step forward and gathered a handful of his shirt front in my fist. "Listen to me, you ugly little crook," I spat in his face, "I'm talking language you can understand. I'm not worried about the cops. If you're under suspicion it's to me. I'm the one that counts, because when I find the one that did it, he dies. Even if I can't prove it, he dies anyway. In fact, I don't even have to be convinced too strongly. Maybe just a few things will point your way, and when they do I'm going after you. Before I'm done I may shoot up a lot of snotty punks like you, but you can bet that one of them will have been the one I was after, and as for the rest, tough luck. They got their noses a little too dirty."

Nobody had talked to him like that the past twenty years. He floundered for words but they didn't come. If he had opened his mouth right then, I would have slammed his teeth down his throat.

Disgusted with the sight of him, I shoved him back toward an end table in time to push myself aside far enough to keep from getting brained. A crockery vase smashed on my shoulder and shattered into a hundred fragments.

I ducked and whirled at the same time. A fist came flying over my head and I blocked it with my left. I didn't wait. I let fly a wicked punch that landed low then came up with the top of my skull and I rammed the point of a jaw with a shattering impact. Hal Kines hit the floor and lay there motionless.

"Wise guy. A fresh kid that tries to bust me from behind. You're certainly not training him right, George. Time was when you stood behind a chopper yourself, now you let a college kid do your blasting, and in a houseful of mirrors he tries to sneak up behind me." He didn't say anything. He found a chair and slid into it, his eyes narrow slits of hate. If he had a rod right then he would have let me have it. He would have died, too. I've had an awful lot of practice sneaking that .45 out from under my arm.

The Kines kid was beginning to stir. I prodded him in the ribs with my toe until he sat up. He was still pretty green around the gills, but not green enough to sneer at me. "You lousy bastard," he said. "Have to fight dirty, don't you."

I reached down and grabbed him under the arm and yanked him to his feet. His eyes bugged. Maybe he thought he was dealing with somebody soft. "Listen, pimple face. Just for the fun of it I ought to slap your fuzzy chin all around this room, but I got things to do. Don't go playing man when you're only a boy. You're pretty big, but I'm three sizes bigger and a hell of a lot tougher and I'll beat the living daylights out of you if you try anything funny again. Now sit down over there."

Kines hit the sofa and stayed there. George must have gotten his second wind because he piped up. "Just a moment, Mr. Hammer. This has gone far enough. I am not without influence at city hall. . . ."

"I know," I cut in. "You'll have me arrested for assault and battery and have my license revoked. Only when you do that, keep a picture in your mind of what your face will look like when I reach you. Someone already worked over your nose, but it's nothing compared to what you'll look like when I get done with it. Now keep your big mouth shut and give me some answers. First, what time did you leave the party?"

"About one or a little after," George said sullenly. That checked with Myrna's version.

"Where did you go after you left?"

"We went downstairs to Hal's car and drove straight home."

"Who's we?"

"Hal, Myrna and myself. We dropped her off at her apartment and came here after putting the car in the garage. Ask Hal, he'll verify it."

Hal looked at me. It was easy to see that he was worried. Evidently this was the first time he had been mixed up in anything so deep. Murders don't appeal to anyone.

I continued with my questioning. "Then what?"

"Oh, for Pete's sake, we had a highball and went to bed. What else do you think we did?" Hal said.

"I don't know. Maybe you sleep together." Hal stood up in front of me, his face a red mask of fury. I put my mitt in his face and shoved him back on the sofa. "Or maybe," I went on, "you don't sleep together. Which means that either one of you had plenty of time to take the car back out and make the run to town to knock off Jack and get back here without anyone noticing it. If you do sleep together you both could have done it. See what I mean?

"If either of you think you're clean you'd better think again. I'm not the only one that has a mind that can figure out angles. Right now Pat Chambers has it all figured out on paper. He'll be around soon, so you'd better be expecting him. And if either of you are tapped for the hot seat, you'd do a lot better by letting Pat pick you up. At least that way you'll live through a trial."

"Someone calling me?" a voice said from the doorway. I spun

around. Pat Chambers was framed in the hardwood paneling wearing his ever-present grin.

I waved him over. "Yeah. You're the main topic of conversation around here at this minute." George Kalecki got up from the overstuffed cushions and walked to Pat. His old bluster was back.

"Officer, I demand the arrest of this man at once," he fairly shouted. "He broke into my home and insulted me and my guest. Look at the bruise on his jaw. Tell him what happened, Hal."

Hal saw me watching him. He saw Pat standing ten feet away from me with his hands in his pockets and apparently no desire to stop what might happen. It suddenly hit him that Jack had been a cop and Pat was a cop and Jack had been killed. And you don't kill a cop and get away with it. "Nothing happened," he said.

"You stinking little liar!" Kalecki turned on him. "Tell the truth! Tell how he threatened us. What are you afraid of, this dirty two-bit shamus?"

"No, George," I said quietly, "he's afraid of this." I swung on him with all of my hundred and ninety pounds. My fist went in up to the wrist in his stomach. He flopped to the floor vomiting his lungs out, his face gradually turning purple. Hal just looked. For a second I could have sworn I saw a satisfied leer cross his swollen face.

I took Pat by the arm. "Coming?" I asked him.

"Yeah, nothing more to do here."

Outside Pat's car was drawn up under the covered portico. We climbed in and he started it up and drove around the house to the graveled driveway to the highway and turned south toward the city. Neither of us had spoken until I asked him, "Get an earful back there?"

He gave me a glance and nodded. "Yeah, I was outside the door while you were going through your spiel. Guess you laid it out the same way I did."

"By the way," I added, "don't get the idea I'm slipping. I was onto the tail you put on me. What did he do, call from the front gate or the filling station where I left my heap?"

"From the station," he answered. "He couldn't catch on to why the hike and called for instructions. By the way. Why did you walk a mile and a half to his house?"

"That ought to be easy, Pat. Kalecki probably left instructions not to admit me after he read that piece in the papers. I came in over the wall. Here's the station. Pull up."

Pat slid the car off the road to the cindered drive. My car was still alongside the stucco house. I pointed to the grey-suited man sitting inside asleep. "Your tail. Better wake him up."

Pat got out and shook the guy. He came to with a silly grin. Pat motioned in my direction. "He was on to you, chum. Maybe you had better change your technique."

The guy looked puzzled. "On to me? Hell, he never gave me a tumble."

"Nuts," I said. "Your rod sticks out of your back pocket like a sore thumb. I've been in this game awhile myself, you know."

I climbed into my buggy and turned it over. Pat stuck his head in the window and asked, "You still going ahead on your own, Mike?"

The best I could do was nod. "Natch. What else?"

"Then you'd better follow me in to town. I have something that might interest you."

He got in the squad car and slid out of the cinders to the highway. My tail pulled out behind Pat and I followed him. Pat was playing it square so far. He was using me for bait, but I didn't mind. It was like using a trout for bait to catch flies as far as I was concerned. But he was sticking too close to me to make the game any fun. Whether he was keeping me from being blasted or just making sure I didn't knock off any prominent Joes whom I suspected I couldn't say.

The article in the paper didn't have enough time to work. The killer wouldn't be flushed as quickly as that. Whoever pulled the trigger was a smart apple. Too damned smart. He must have considered me if he was in his right mind at all. He had to consider the cops even if it was an ordinary job. But this was a cop killing which made it worse. I was sure of one thing though, I'd be on the kill list for sure, especially after I made the rounds of everyone connected with it.

So far, I couldn't find anything on Kalecki or Kines. No motive yet. That would come later. They both had the chance to knock off Jack. George Kalecki wasn't what people thought him to be. His finger was still in the rackets. Possibilities there. Where Hal came in was something else again. He was tied up in some way. Maybe not. Maybe so. I'd find out.

My thoughts wandered around the general aspects of the case without reaching any conclusions. Pat went through the city sans benefit of a siren, unlike a lot of coppers, and we finally pulled up to the curb in front of his precinct station.

Upstairs he pulled open the bottom drawer of his desk and drew out a pint of bourbon from a lunch box. He handed me a man-sized slug of the stuff and set up one for himself. I poured mine down in one gulp.

"Want another?"

"Nope. Want some information. What were you going to tell me?" He went over to a filing cabinet and drew out a folder. I noticed the label. It read, "Myrna Devlin."

Pat sat down and shook out the contents. The dossier was complete. It had everything on her that I had and more. "What's the angle, Pat?" I knew he was getting at something. "Are you connecting Myrna with this? If you are you're barking up the wrong tree."

"Perhaps. You see, Mike, when Jack first found Myrna trying to go over the railing of the bridge, he treated her like any other narcotic case. He took her to the emergency ward of the hospital." Pat rose and shoved his hands in his pockets. His mouth talked, but I could see that his mind was deep in thought. "It was through constant contact with her that he fell in love. It was real enough for him. He saw all the bad side of her before he saw the good. If he could love her then he could love her anytime."

"I don't follow, Pat. I know Myrna as well as Jack did. If you smear her all over the papers as a number-one candidate for the hot squat you and me are going to have it out."

"Don't fly off the handle, Mike. There's more to it than that. After she was released, she made Jack promise not to follow it up any further. He agreed."

"I know," I cut in, "I was there that night."

"Well, Jack held up his end to her all right, but that didn't take in the whole department. Narcotics comes under a separate bureau. The case was turned over to them. Myrna didn't know anything about it, but while she was out, she talked. We had a steno taking down every word she said and she said plenty. Narcotics was able to snare a ring that was operating around the city, but when they made the raid there was some shooting, and during it the one guy that would have been able to spill the beans caught one in the head and the cycle stopped there."

"That's news to me, Pat."

"Yeah, you were in the army then. It took awhile to track the outfit down, nearly a year. It didn't stop even then. The outfit was working interstate and the feds were in on it. They laid off Myrna when they went into her history. She was a small-town girl here in the city to break into show business. Unfortunately, she got mixed up with the wrong outfit and got put on the stuff by one of her roommates. Their contact was a guy who was paying for protection as a bookie, but who used the cover to peddle dope. His guardian angel was a politician who now occupies a cozy cell in Ossining on the Hudson.

"The head of the outfit was a shrewd operator. No one knew or saw him. Transactions were made by mail. Dope was sent in to post-office boxes, very skillfully disguised. In each box was a number to send the cash to. That turned out to be a box somewhere, too."

That I couldn't figure. Pat turned and sat down again before he went on, but I beat him to it with a question.

"Something screwy, Pat. The whole thing's backwards. The stuff is usually paid for in advance, with the peddlers hoping they come through with enough decks to make money on it."

Pat lit a butt and nodded vigorously. "Exactly. That's one reason why we had trouble. Undoubtedly there's stuff sitting in post-office boxes right now loaded to the brims with the junk. It isn't an amateur's touch, either. The stuff came in too regularly. The source was plentiful. We managed to dig up a few old containers that hadn't been destroyed by the receiver and there were no two postmarks alike."

"That wouldn't be hard to work if it was a big outfit."

"Apparently they had no trouble. But we had operatives in the towns the stuff was sent from and they went over the places with a fine-tooth comb. Nothing was turned up. They checked the transient angle since it was the only way it could have been done. Busses and trains went through these towns, and it's possible that the packages could have been dropped off by a person posing as a traveler. Each place was used once. So there was no way of telling where the next one was coming from."

"I get the picture, Pat. Since the last outfit was pulled, have they found any other sources?"

"Some. But nothing they could connect with the last. Most of it was petty stuff with some hospital attendant sneaking it out of stock and peddling it on the outside."

"So far you haven't told me where Myrna comes into this. I appreciate the information, but we're not getting anyplace. What you've given me is stricly police stuff."

Pat gave me a long, searching glance. His eyes were screwed up tight like he was thinking. I knew that look well. "Tell me," he said, "hasn't it occurred to you that Jack, being a cop, could have welshed on his promise to Myrna? He hated crooks and sneaks, but most of all he hated the dirty rats that used people like Myrna to line their own pockets."

"So what?" I asked.

"So this. He was in on things in the beginning. He might have been holding back something on us. Or he might have gotten something from Myrna we didn't know about. Either he spoke up at the wrong moment or he didn't. But somebody was afraid of what he knew and bumped him." I yawned. I hated to disillusion Pat but he was wrong. "Fellow, you are really mixed up. Let me show you where. First, classify all murders. There are only a few. War, Passion, Self-Protection, Insanity, Profit and Mercy Killings. There are some others, but these are enough. To me it looks like Jack was killed either for profit or self-protection. I don't doubt but what he had something on someone. It must have been something he had known all along and suddenly realized its importance, or it was something he recently found out. You know how active he was in police work even though he was disabled and attached to the job with the insurance company.

"Whatever it was, he apparently wanted to make a choice. That's why you heard nothing about it. The killer had to have something he had, and killed to get it. But you searched the place, didn't you?" Pat agreed with a movement of the eyes. "And there was nothing removed, was there?" He shook his head. "Then," I went on, "unless it was something Jack had outside, which I doubt, it wasn't a killing for profit. The killer knew that Jack had some poop which would mean exposure or worse. To protect himself, the killer knocked Jack off. Self-protection."

I picked up my battered hat from the desk and stretched. "Got to blow, pal. Since I'm not on an expense account or a salary, this is one job I can't afford to lose time on. Thanks for the try, anyway. If I turn anything up I'll let you know."

"How long after?" Pat said with a smile.

"Just long enough to keep the jump on you," I shot back at him. I fished for a smoke and pulled a wreck of a butt from my pocket, waved so long to Pat and walked out. My tail was waiting for me, trying to look inconspicuous in a crowd of cigar-smoking detectives in the anteroom. As I stepped outside I flattened myself into a niche in the brick wall. The guy came out, stopped and looked frantically both ways up and down the street. I stepped out and tapped him on the shoulder.

"Got a light?" I asked, flipping the ancient butt between my lips. He turned beet-red and lit me. "Instead of playing cops and robbers," I told him, "why not just walk along with me?"

He didn't quite know what to say, but got out an "Okay." It sounded more like a growl. The two of us ambled over to my car. He got in and I slid under the wheel. There was no use trying to talk to the guy. I couldn't get a word out of him. When I hit the main stem, I went down a side street past a little hotel. After I pulled up in front of it, I got out with my tail right behind me, went through the revolving door, kept right on going until I was outside where I went in. That left my tail still in the door. I bent down and stuck a rubber wedge I had taken from my car window under the door and walked back to the car. Inside the door, the cop was pounding on the glass and calling me dirty names. If he wanted me, he had to go out the back door and around the street. I saw the clerk grinning. That wasn't the first time I had used his hotel for that gag. All the way downtown my window shook like it would fall out, which reminded me that I had better get some more wedges in case I was tailed again.

chapter 4

THE anteroom was ultramodern, but well appointed. Chairs that looked angular were really very comfortable. Whoever decorated the interior had a patient's mental comfort well in mind. The walls were an indescribable shade of olive, cleverly matched with a dull-finished set of drapes. The windows admitted no light, instead, the soft glow came from hidden bulbs installed directly into the wall. On the floor an ankle-thick carpet muffled any sound of footsteps. From somewhere came the muted tones of a string quartet. I could have fallen asleep right there if the secretary who had given me the telephone brushoff didn't motion me over to the desk. From her tone it was evident that she knew that I was no patient.

With a full day's growth of beard and the wrinkled ruin of a suit I had on, I was lower than the janitor in her estimation.

She inclined her head toward the door behind her and said, "Miss Manning will see you now. Please go in." With special emphasis on the please. When I went past her she drew back slightly.

"Don't worry, honey," I told her out of the corner of my mouth, "I won't bite. This is just a disguise." I yanked open the door and went in.

She was better than her picture. She was delicious. There was a lot about her that couldn't be put into words. Charlotte Manning was sitting at her desk, hands folded in front of her as if she were listening for something. Beautiful was a poor description. She was what you would expect to find in a painting if each of the world's greatest artists added their own special technique to produce a masterpiece.

Her hair was almost white as I thought. It fell in such soft curls you wanted to bury your face in it. Each of her features was modeled exquisitely. A smooth forehead melted into alive, hazel eyes, framed in the symmetrical curves of naturally brown eyebrows, studded with long, moist lashes.

The dress she wore was not at all revealing, being a long-sleeved black business garb, but what it attempted to conceal was pure loveliness. Her breasts fought the dress as valiantly as they had the bathing suit. I could only imagine how the rest of her looked since the desk blocked my vision.

All this I saw in the three seconds it took to walk across the room. I doubt if she saw any change in my expression, but she could have sued me if she knew what went on in my mind.

"Good morning, Mr. Hammer. Please sit down." Her voice was

like liquid. I wondered what she could do if she put a little passion in it. Plenty, I bet. It wasn't hard to see why she was a successful psychiatrist. Here was a woman anyone could tell their troubles to.

I sat down in the chair beside her and she swung around to meet my eyes with a steady, direct gaze. "I presume you are here on police business?"

"Not exactly. I'm a private detective."

"Oh." When she said that her voice held none of the usual contempt or curiosity I find when I tell that to someone. Instead, it was as if I had given her a pertinent piece of information.

"Is it about the death of Mr. Williams?" she asked.

"Uh-huh. He was a close buddy of mine. I'm conducting a sort of personal investigation of my own."

She looked at me quizzically at first, then, "Oh, yes. I read your statement in the papers. As a matter of fact, I attempted to analyze your reasoning. I've always been interested in things of that sort."

"And what conclusion did you reach?"

Charlotte surprised me. "I'm afraid I justify you, although several of my former professors would condemn me if I made that statement public." I saw what she meant. There's a school of thought that believes anyone who kills is the victim of a moment's insanity, no matter what the reason for the killing.

"How can I help you?" she went on.

"By answering a few questions. First, what time did you get to the party that night?"

"Roughly, about eleven. I was held up by a visit to a patient."

"What time did you leave?"

"Around one. We left together."

"Then where did you go?"

"I had my car downstairs. Esther and Mary Bellemy drove with me. We went to the Chicken Bar and had a sandwich. We left there at one forty-five. I remember the time because we were the only ones there and they were getting ready to close at two. I dropped the twins off at their hotel, then went straight to my apartment. I reached there about a quarter after two. I remember the time there, too, since I had to reset my alarm clock."

"Anybody see you come into the apartment?"

Charlotte gave me the cutest little laugh. "Yes, Mr. District Attorney. My maid. She even tucked me into bed as usual. She would have heard me go out, too, for the only door to my apartment has a chime on it that rings whenever the door opens, and Kathy is a very light sleeper."

I couldn't help but grin at that. "Has Pat Chambers been here to see you already?"

"This morning, but much earlier." She laughed again. Shivers went through me when she did that. She radiated sex in every manner and gesture. "What is more," she continued, "he came, he saw, and he suspected. By now he must be checking my story."

"Pat's not letting any grass grow under his feet," I mused. "Did he mention me at all?"

"Not a word. A very thorough man. He represents efficiency. I like him."

"One thing more. When did you make the acquaintance of Jack Williams?"

"I'm afraid I'm not at liberty to reveal that."

I shook my head. "If it was in reference to Myrna, you needn't be. I was on the ground floor there."

She seemed surprised at that. But I knew Jack had kept the entire affair of Myrna's past as close to his vest as possible. "Well," she said, "that was it. He called me in under advice from a doctor to attend Myrna. She had suffered a severe shock. I doubt if you can comprehend what it means to one addicted to narcotics to go 'cold turkey' as they call it. It means an immediate and complete removal from the source of the drug. The mental strain is terrific. They have violent convulsions, their bodies endure the most racking pain there is. Nerve ends eaten raw are exposed to unbelievable torture, and you can give them no relief. Quite often they destroy themselves in fits of madness.

"The cure is far from an easy one. Having made the decision, they are separated from outside contact in padded cells. During the earlier stages of it, they change their minds and beg to be given the drug. Later the pain and tension mount to such dizzy heights that they are completely unrational. All the while, their body fights the effects of the drug, and it emerges finally either cured or unfit to continue life. In Myrna's case, she lived through it. Jack was worried what this would do to her mentally and called me. I treated her while she was undergoing the cure, and afterwards. Since she was released I have never visited her in a professional capacity."

"Well, I guess that's all then. I do have some other things I would like to discuss with you about the case. But I want to do a little checking first."

She gave me another of those smiles. Any more of them and she'd find out what it was like to be kissed from under a set of whiskers. "If it's about the time element of my story—or should I say alibi?—then I suggest you hurry over to my apartment before my maid goes on her weekly shopping spree."

The woman knew all the answers. I tried to keep my face

straight, but it was too much work. I broke out my lopsided grin and picked up my hat. "That's partly it. Guess I don't trust anybody."

Charlotte rose and gave me the look at her legs I'd been waiting for. "I understand," she remarked. "To a man friendship is a much greater thing than to a woman."

"Especially when that friend gave an arm to save my life," I said.

A puzzled frown creased her forehead. "So you're the one." It was almost a gasp. "I didn't know, but I'm glad I do now. I have heard so much about you from Jack, but they were stories in the third person. He never mentioned a thing about his arm, although Myrna later told me why he lost it."

"Jack didn't want to embarrass me. But that's only part of the reason why I'm going to get his murderer. He was my friend even before that."

"I hope you get him," she said sincerely. "I truly hope you do."

"I will," I said.

We stood there a moment just looking at each other, then I caught myself. "I have to leave now. I'll see you soon."

Her breath seemed to catch in her throat a moment before she said softly, "Very soon, I trust." I was hoping that light in her eyes meant what I thought it did when she said it.

I parked a few feet away from the blue canopy of the apartment house. The doorman, for once conservatively dressed, opened the door of my car without wrinkling his mouth in disgust. I gave him a nod and went into the outer foyer.

The name over the bell was stamped in aluminum. "Manning Charlotte," it read, without a series of degrees following it like the doctor's below. That guy must have had a letter complex. I rang the bell and walked in when the buzzer sounded.

She lived on the fourth floor, in a suite facing the street. A coal-black maid in a white uniform answered the door. "Mistah Hammah?" she asked me.

"Yeah, how didja know?"

"De police gennimuns in de front room was 'specting you. Come in, please." Sure enough, there was Pat sprawled in a chair by the window.

"Hi, Mike," he called. I threw my hat on an end table and sat down on a hassock beside him.

"What did you find, Pat?"

"Her story checks. A neighbor saw her come in at the proper time; her maid confirmed it." For once I was relieved. "I knew you'd be along, so I just parked the carcass until you showed up. By the way, I wish you'd be a little easier on the men I detail to keep track of you."

"Easier, hell. Keep 'em off my neck. Either that or get an expert."

"Just for your own protection, Mike."

"Nuts. You know me better than that. I can take care of myself." Pat let his head fall back and closed his eyes. I looked around the room. Like her office, Charlotte Manning's apartment was furnished in excellent taste. It had a casual air that made it look lived in, yet everything was in order. It wasn't large; then too it had no reason to be. Living alone with one maid, a few rooms was all that was necessary. Several good paintings adorned the walls, hanging above shelves that were well stocked with books of all kinds. I noticed one bookcase that held nothing but volumes on psychology. At one end of the room a framed diploma was the only ornament. A wide hallway opened off the living room and led to a bedroom and the kitchen, with a bathroom opposite. Beside the foyer was the maid's room. Here the color scheme was not conducive to mental peace, but designed to add color and gaiety to its already beautiful occupant. Directly opposite the hassock I was parked on was a sofa, a full six feet long. It gave me ideas, which I quickly ignored. It was no time to play wolf. Yet.

I nudged Pat with my foot. "Don't let's be going to sleep, chum. You're on taxpayers' time."

He came out of his reverie with a start. "Only giving you time to size things up, junior. Let's roll."

Kathy, the maid, came scurrying in when she heard us making sounds of leaving. She opened the door for us and I heard the sound of the chimes Charlotte had spoken of. "Does the gong go off when the bell rings too?" I asked her.

"Yassuh, or when de do' opens, too."

"Why?"

"Well, suh, when I'se not to home, Miss Charlotte has to answer de do'. Sometimes when she's busy in de blackroom de bell rings and she just opens de lock. Den when de visitors come up she knows when dey comes in. She can't leave in de middle of her work in de blackroom to answer both de bell and de do'."

I looked at Pat and he looked at me. "What's the blackroom?" I practically demanded.

Kathy jumped like she was shot. "Why, where she makes pitchers from de fillums," she answered. Pat and I left feeling a little foolish. So Charlotte made a hobby of photography. I reminded myself to brush up on details so we'd have something to speak about the next time we met. Besides that, I mean.

chapter 5

DOWNSTAIRS, Pat and I went across the street to a tiny delicatessen and sat in a booth with two bottles of beer. He asked me if I had gotten anywhere yet and I had to give him a negative answer.

"What about motive?" I put to him. "I'm up the creek on that angle, mainly because I haven't looked into it. When I get all the case histories down I'll begin on the motive. But did you dig up anything yet?"

"Not yet," Pat answered. "Ballistics checked on the slug and it came from an unidentified .45. According to the experts, the barrel was nearly new. We followed that up by inquiring into the sale of all guns, but got nowhere. Only two had been sold, both to store owners who were recently robbed. We took some samples of the slugs, but they didn't match."

"For that matter it might have been a gun sold some time ago, but unfired until recently," I said.

"We thought of that, too. Records still don't account for it. None of those at the party have ever owned a gun to our knowledge."

"Officially," I added.

"Yes, that's a possibility. It isn't hard to come in possession of a gun."

"What about the silencer? The killer was no novice about firearms. A silencer plus a dumdum. He wanted to make sure Jack died—not too fast. Just definitely died."

"No trace of that, either. Where it may have come from is a rifle. There are a few makes of rifle silencers that can be adjusted to a .45."

We sipped the beer slowly, each of us thinking hard. It was a full two minutes before Pat remembered something and said, "Oh, yeah, almost forgot. Kalecki and the Kines kid moved into an apartment in town this morning."

That was news. "What for?"

"Someone took a shot at him through his window late last night. Missed by a hair. It was a .45 slug, too. We checked it with the one that killed Jack. It was the same gun."

I almost choked on my beer. "You almost forgot," I said with a smirk.

"Oh, and one other thing."

"What?"

"He thinks you did it."

I banged my glass down on the table so hard Pat jumped.

"Why, that dirty snivelling louse! That does it. This time I'll smash his face all over the place!"

"There you go, racing your motor again, Mike. Sit down and pipe down. As he said, he wasn't without a little influence at city hall, and they made us look into you. But don't forget, you've knocked off a few undesirable citizens before and the slugs from your gun were photographed. We keep all the prints and tried in the worst way to match 'em, but they don't match. Besides, we knew where you were last night. They raided the joint ten minutes after you left."

I got kind of red in the face and sat down. "You got one hell of a way of breaking things to me, Pat. Now let's quit the joking and tell me where Kalecki and company moved to."

Pat grinned. "They live right around the corner in the same apartment hotel the Bellemy twins occupy, but on the second floor. The Midworth Arms."

"Have you been there yet?"

"Not to see the twins. I saw George and Hal, though. Had quite a time telling him that it would do no good to place a charge against you for assault and battery after the other night. Didn't take much talking, either. Evidently he's heard a lot about the way you operate, but just likes to keep his own courage up with a lot of talk."

Both of us poured down the remainder of the beer and got up to leave. I outfumbled Pat and got stuck for the check. Next time he'd buy. Cop or no cop. We parted outside the door, and as soon as he took off I started around the corner for the Midworth Arms. I wanted to get the low-down when anyone accused me of murder—attempted or successful. The real reason why Pat was sure it wasn't me was because the killer missed. I wouldn't have.

I knew Kalecki probably had tipped the doorman and the super off not to admit me, so I didn't bother messing with them. Instead I walked in like a regular resident and took the elevator to the second floor. The operator was a skinny runt in his late twenties who wore a built-in leer. I was the only one in the car, and when we stopped I pulled a bill from my pocket and showed him the color of it.

"Kalecki. George Kalecki. He's new in this dump. What apartment and the green is yours," I said.

He gave me a careful going over, that one. Finally put his tongue in his cheek and said, "You must be that Hammer mug. He gimme a ten not to spot him for you."

I opened my coat and pulled my .45 from its holster. The kid's eyes popped when he saw it. "I *am* that Hammer mug, junior," I told him, "and if you don't spot him for me *I'm* giving you this." I motioned toward his teeth with the gun barrel.

"Front 206," he said hastily. My bill was a five. I rolled it up in a ball and poked it in his wide-opened mouth, then shoved the rod back.

"The next time remember me. And in the meantime, act like a clam or I'll open you up like one."

"Y-yes, sir." He practically leaped back in the car and slammed the door shut.

Two oh six was down the hall, the apartment facing on the street. I knocked, but there was no answer. Hardly breathing, I put my ear against the wood paneling of the door and kept it there. That way the wood acts as a sounding board, and any noise made inside is magnified a hundred times. That is, except this time. Nobody was home. Just to be sure, I slid a note under the door, then walked away and took the stairs down to the first landing. There I took off my shoes and tiptoed back up. The note was still sticking out exactly as I had placed it.

Instead of fooling around I brought out a set of skeleton keys. The third one did it. I snapped the deadlock on the door behind me—just in case.

The apartment was furnished. None of Kalecki's personal stuff was in the front room except a picture of himself on the mantel when he was younger. I walked into the bedroom. It was a spacious place, with two chests of drawers and a table. But there was only one bed. So they did sleep together. I had to laugh even if I did mention it to get a rise out of them before.

A suitcase was under the bed. I opened that first. On top of six white shirts a .45 was lying with two spare clips beside it. Man, oh man, that caliber gun is strictly for professionals, and they were turning up all over the place. I sniffed the barrel, but it was clean. As far as I could tell, it hadn't been fired for a month. I wiped my prints off and put the gun back.

There wasn't much in the chests of drawers, either. Hal Kines had a photo album that showed him engaging in nearly every college sport there is. A lot of the shots were of women, and some of them weren't half bad, that is if you like them tall and on the thin side. Me, I like 'em husky. Toward the end of the book were several showing Kalecki and Hal together. In one they were fishing. Another was taken alongside a car in camping clothes. It was the third one that interested me.

Both Hal and Kalecki were standing outside a store. In this one

47

Hal wasn't dressed like a college kid at all. In fact, he looked quite the businessman. But that wasn't the point—yet. In the window behind him was one of those news releases they plant in stores facing the street that are made up of a big photo with a caption below it. There were two. One was indiscernible, but the other was the burning of the *Morro Castle*. And the *Morro Castle* went up in flames eight years ago. Yet here was Hal Kines looking older than he looked now.

I didn't get any more time to look around. I heard the elevator doors slam and I walked into the front room. When I got there someone was fiddling at the lock. There was a steady stream of curses before I clicked up the deadlock and opened the door. "Come in, George," I said.

He looked more scared than amazed. Apparently he really believed that it was me who took the shot at him. Hal was behind him ready to run as soon as I made one move. George recovered first.

"Where do you get off breaking into my apartment. This time—"

"Oh, shut up and come in. It's just as monotonous for me. If you'd stay home awhile, you'd be better off." The two of them stamped into the bedroom. When he came out he was red as a beet. I didn't give him a chance to accuse me of anything.

"Why all the artillery?" I asked him.

"For guys like you," he snarled, "for guys that try potting me through a window. Besides, I have a permit to carry it."

"Okay, you got a permit. Just be sure you know who you use that rod on."

"Don't worry, I'll give you a warning first. Now, if you don't mind, will you tell me what you are doing here?"

"Sure, sonny. I want the low-down on the bang, bang. Since I was the one accused of it, I'd like to know just what I was supposed to have done."

George slid a cigar from its wrapper and inserted it in a holder. He took his time lighting it up before he spoke.

"You seem to have police connections," he said finally. "Why don't you ask them?"

"Because I don't like secondhand information. And if you're smart you'll talk. That gun was the killer's gun, and I want the killer. You know that. But that isn't all. The killer made one try and missed, so you can bet your boots there'll be another."

Kalecki took the cigar out of his mouth. Little lines of fear were racing around his eyes. The guy was scared. He tried to hide it, but he didn't do very well. A nervous tic tugged at the corner of his mouth.

"I still see nothing I can tell you that would help. I was sitting in the big chair by the window. The first thing I knew the glass shattered beside me and the bullet hit the back of the chair. I dropped to the floor and crawled to the wall to be out of sight of whoever fired the shot."

"Why?" I said slowly.

"Why? To save myself, of course. You don't think I was just going to sit there and get shot at, do you?" Kalecki gave me a look of contempt but I ignored it.

"You don't get the point, George," I told him. "Why were you shot at to begin with?"

Little beads of sweat were popping out on his forehead. He wiped his brow nervously. "How should I know? I've made enemies in my time."

"This was a very particular enemy, George. This one killed

Jack, too, and he's coming back after you. He may not miss the next time. Why are you on his list?"

He was really jumpy now. "I—I don't know. Honest I don't." He was almost apologetic the way he spoke now. "I tried to think it out but I don't get anywhere. That's why I moved to the city. Where I was, anyone could get to me. At least here there are other people around."

I leaned forward. "You didn't think enough. You and Jack had something in common. What was it? What did you know that Jack did? What did you have on somebody that Jack might have stumbled to? When you answer that question you'll have your killer. Now do I bang your head on the floor to help you remember or do you do it yourself?"

He stood up straight and paced across the room. The thought of being on a kill list had him half bugs. He just wasn't as young as he used to be. This sort of thing got him down.

"I can't say. If there's anything, it's a mistake. I didn't know Jack long. Hal knew him. He met him through Miss Manning. If you can figure out a tie-up in there I'll be glad to tell you what I know. Do you think I want to get knocked off?"

That was an angle I had forgotten about. Hal Kines was still sitting in the armchair beside the mantlepiece dragging heavily on a cigarette. For an athlete he wasn't holding to training rules at all. I still couldn't get the picture of Hal out of my mind. The one taken eight years ago. He was only a young punk, but that shot made him look like an old man. I don't know. Maybe it was an abandoned store that had the picture in it for years.

"Okay, Hal, let's hear what you know." The kid turned his head toward me, giving me an excellent view of his Greek-god profile.

"George mentioned everything."

"How do you know Miss Manning?" I asked him. "When did you meet her? After all, a babe like that plays ball in a bigger league than you can pay admission to see."

"Oh, she came to school last year and gave a lecture on practical psychology. That's what I'm majoring in. She had several students visit her clinic in New York to see her methods. I was one of them. She became interested in me and assisted me no end. That's all."

It wasn't hard to see why she'd become interested in him. It made me mad to think of it, but he could have been right. Maybe it was purely professional interest. After all, a woman like that could have just about any male she wanted, including me.

I went on. "And what about Jack? When did you meet him?"

"Shortly afterwards. Miss Manning took me to his apartment for supper with him and Myrna. I got involved in a drunken brawl right after a football game. It was the last one of the season and all training rules were off. I guess we all went a bit too far, but we wrecked a joint. Jack knew the proprietor and instead of turning us in, made us pay for the place. The following week I was studying the case history of a homicidal maniac in the city wards when I met him again. He was glad to see me and we had dinner together. We became rather good friends in a short time. I was glad to know him, because he helped me immensely. The type of work I was doing involved visits to places where I ordinarily would not have access to, but with his help I managed to get to them all."

For the life of me I couldn't make anything out of it. Jack never spoke too much about anyone. Our association had started by having an interest in police work and our friendship had developed over firing ranges, ballistics tables and fingerprint indexes. Even in the army we had thought about it. Life on the side was only incidental. He had mentioned his friends. That's about all. Myrna I knew very well. Kalecki from his underworld contacts. The Bellemy twins from the newspapers mostly, and the short time I had seen them before.

There was nothing more to be gained by hanging around here. I slapped my hat back on and walked toward the door. Neither of them thought to say so long, so I stepped out and slammed the door as hard as I could. Outside I wondered when George had gotten hold of the .45. Pat had said none of those at the party had ever owned a gun. Yet George had one and a permit to carry it. Or at least he said so. Well, if anything cropped up where a .45 was involved, I'd know where to look first.

The Bellemy twins lived on the fifth floor. Their apartment was in the same position as Kalecki's. The only difference was that they answered the bell. The door had a chain lock on the inside and a plain, but vaguely pretty face was meeting mine through the six-inch opening.

"Yes?"

I couldn't tell which of the twins I was speaking to, so I said, "Miss Bellemy?" She nodded. "I'm Mr. Hammer, private investigator. I'm working on the Williams case. Could you . . ."

"Why, of course." The door closed and the chain removed from the lock. When the door opened again, I was facing a woman that had athlete written all over her. Her skin was brown from the sun except for the wrinkle spots beside her eyes, and her arms and shoulders were as smooth-muscled as a statue's. This one certainly didn't have justice done her by her photos. For a moment it struck me why they were having any trouble finding husbands. As far as I could see, there wasn't anything wrong with this particular twin that the money she had couldn't cover. Plenty of guys would take her without any cash settlement at all.

"Won't you come in?"

"Thank you." I stepped inside and surveyed the place. Not much different from Kalecki's, but it had a light perfume smell instead of a cigar odor. She led me to a pair of divans separated by a coffee table and waved toward one. I sat down and she took the other.

"Now what is it you wish to see me about?"

"Perhaps you'd better tell me which Miss Bellemy I'm speaking to so I won't get my twins crossed."

"Oh, I'm Mary," she laughed. "Esther has gone shopping, which means she's gone for the day."

"Well, I guess you can tell me all I need to know. Has Mr. Chambers been to see you yet?"

"Yes. And he told me to expect you, too."

"I won't have much to ask. You knew Jack before the war, didn't you?" She acknowledged with a nod. "Did you notice anything particular the night of the party?" I continued.

"No, nothing. Light drinking and a little dancing. I saw Jack talking rather earnestly to Myrna a few times, and once he and Mr. Kines went out in the kitchen for about fifteen minutes, but they came back laughing as though they had been telling jokes."

"Did any of the others team up at all?"

"Umm, no, not to speak of. Myrna and Charlotte had a conference for a while, but the boys broke it up when the dancing started. I think they were talking about Myrna's wedding plans."

"What about afterwards?"

"We had a bite to eat, then came home. Both of us had forgotten our keys as usual and had to wake the super up to let us in. Both of us went right to bed. I knew nothing about the murder until a reporter awakened us with a phone call to get a statement. We expected a visit from the police at once and stayed at home to receive them, but no one came until today."

She stopped short and cocked her head a little. "Oh," she said, "you must excuse me. I left the water running in the tub." She ran to the narrow hallway and disappeared into the bathroom. Maybe I was getting old. I didn't hear any water running.

A couple of magazines were lying in a rack beside the divan. I picked one up and thumbed through it, but it was one of those pattern and fashion jobs without any pictures and I dropped it. Two new copies of *Confessions* were on the bottom of the pile. These were better than the rest, but still the same old story. One was a humdinger about a gal that meets a detective in a big city. He does her dirt and she tries to throw herself in front of a subway train. Some nice young jerk grabs her in time and makes a respectable woman of her.

I had just gotten to where he was leading her to the justice of the peace when Mary Bellemy came back. Only this time she made my head swim. Instead of the grey suit she had on before, she wore a sheer pink negligee that was designed with simplicity as the motif. Her hair was down out of the roll and her face looked clean and strong.

Whether or not she planned it I don't know, but she passed momentarily in front of the light streaming in from the window and I could see through everything she had on. And it wasn't much. Just the negligee. She smiled and sat down beside me. I moved over to make some room.

"I'm sorry I had to leave you, but the water wouldn't stay hot very long."

"That's all right, most women take all day at that."

She laughed again. "Not me. I was too anxious to hear more about this case you're working on." She crossed her legs and leaned forward to pick a cigarette from the box on the table. I had to turn my head. At this stage of the game I couldn't afford to get wrapped up with a love life. Besides, I wanted to see Charlotte later.

"Smoke?" she offered.

"No thanks." She leaned back against the divan and blew a ring at the ceiling.

"What else can I tell you? I can speak both for my sister and myself since we were together until the next evening." The sight of her in that carelessly draped sheer fabric kept my mind from what she was saying. "Of course, you can check with my sister later," she added, "exactly as Mr. Chambers did."

"No, that won't be necessary. Those details are minor. What I'm after now are the seemingly unimportant ones. Personality conflicts. Things you might have noticed about Jack the past few days. Any remark that might have been passed or something you overheard."

"I'm afraid I can't help you there. I'm not very good at eaves-dropping and I don't collect gossip. My sister and I have remained fairly isolated in our home, that is, until we came to town. Our circle of friendship reaches out to our neighbors who like isolation as much as we do. Rarely do we entertain guests from the city."

Mary drew her legs up under her on the divan and turned on her side to face me. During the process the negligee fell open, but she took her time to draw it shut. Deliberately, she let my eyes feast on her lovely bosom. What I could see of her stomach was smooth parallel rows of light muscles, almost like a man's. I licked my lips and said, "How long do you expect to remain in town?"

She smiled. "Just long enough so Esther can get her shopping spree over with. Her main joy in living is wearing pretty clothes, regardless of whether or not she's seen in them."

"And yours?"

"My main joy in living is living." Two weeks ago I couldn't picture her saying that, but I could now. Here was a woman to whom time and place didn't mean a damn thing.

"Tell me," I started, "how can you tell the difference between you and your sister?"

"One of us has a small strawberry birthmark on the right hip."

"Which one?"

"Why don't you find out?" Brother, this girl was asking for trouble.

"Not today. I have work to do." I stood up and stretched.

"Don't be a sissy," she said.

Her eyes were blazing into mine. They were violet eyes, a wild blazing violet. Her mouth looked soft and wet, and provocative. She was making no attempt to keep the negligee on. One shoulder had slipped down and her brown skin formed an interesting contrast with the pink. I wondered how she got her tan. There were no strap marks anywhere. She uncrossed her legs deliberately and squirmed like an overgrown cat, letting the light play with the ripply muscles in her naked thighs.

I was only human. I bent over her, taking her mouth on mine. She was straining in the divan to reach me, her arms tight around my neck. Her body was a hot flame; the tip of her tongue searched for mine. She quivered under my hands wherever I touched her. Now I knew why she hadn't married. One man could never satisfy her. My hand fastened on the hem of the negligee and with one motion flipped it open, leaving her body lean and bare. She let my eyes search every inch of her brown figure.

I grabbed my hat and jammed it on my head. "It must be your sister who has the birthmark," I told her as I rose. "See you later."

I half expected to hear a barrage of nasty words when I went through the door and was disappointed. Instead, I heard a faint, faraway chuckle. I would love to have known how Pat reacted to that act. It had dawned on me all of a sudden that she was left in my path as a sort of booby trap while Pat went on his own way. Huh, I'd wrap that guy up for this little trick. There was a neat tomato down on Third Avenue who loved to play tricks herself, especially against the police. Later, perhaps. . . .

chapter 6

VELDA was still at the office when I got there. When I saw the light on I stopped in front of a mirrored door and gave myself a thorough inspection for lipstick marks. I managed to wipe my mouth clean, but getting it off my white collar was something else again. I could never figure out why the stuff came off women so easy and off the men so hard. Before I fooled around Mary Bellemy again I'd be sure she used a Kleenex first.

I went in whistling. Velda took one look at me and her mouth tightened up. "Now what's the matter?" I could see something was wrong.

"You didn't get it off your ear," she said.

Uh-oh. This gal could be murder when she wanted to. I didn't bother to say anything more, but walked into my office. Velda had laid out a clean shirt for me, and an unwrinkled tie. Sometimes I thought she was a mind reader. I kept a few things handy for emergencies, and she generally knew when that would be.

At a washbowl in the corner I cleaned up a bit, then got into my shirt. Ties always were a problem. Usually Velda was on hand to help me out, but when I heard the door slam I knew I'd have to go it alone.

Downstairs I stopped in at the bar and had a few quick ones. The clock on the wall said it was early, so I picked out an empty booth and parked to spend a few hours. The waiter came over and I told him to bring me a rye and soda every fifteen minutes. This was an old custom and the waiter was used to it.

I dragged a list from my pocket and jotted down a few notes concerning Mary Bellemy. So far, the list was mainly character studies, but things like that can give a good insight into a crime. Actually, I hadn't accomplished much. I had made the rounds of the immediate suspects and had given them a good reason to sweat.

The police were doing things in their own methodical way, no doubt. They certainly weren't the saps a lot of newshawks try to make them. A solution to murder takes time. But this murder meant a race. Pat wasn't going to get the jump on me if I could help it. He'd been to the same places I had, but I bet he didn't know any more.

What we were both searching for was motive. There had to be one—and a good one. Murder doesn't just happen. Murder is planned. Sometimes in haste, but planned nevertheless.

As for the time element, George Kalecki had time to kill Jack. So did Hal Kines. I hated to think of it, but Charlotte Manning did too. Then there was Myrna. She too could have circled back to do it, leaving time to get home unnoticed. That left the Bellemy twins. Perhaps it was accidental, but they established their arrival time by letting the super open the door for them. Nice thinking if it was deliberate. I didn't bother to ask whether they left again or not. I knew the answer would be negative. Twins were peculiar; they were supposed to be uncannily inseparable. I've noticed it before in other sets, so these two wouldn't be any different. If it came to it they would lie, cheat or steal for each other.

I couldn't quite picture Mary Bellemy as being a nymphomaniac though. From all I've read of the two, they were sweet and demure, not young, not old. They kept strictly to themselves, or at least that's what the papers said. What a woman will do when's she's alone with a man in her room is another thing. I was looking forward to seeing Esther Bellemy. That strawberry birthmark ought to prove sort of interesting.

Then there was the potshot at Kalecki. That stumped me. The best thing to do was to take a run up town and check up on his contacts. I signaled the waiter over and asked for a check. The guy frowned at me. I guess he wasn't used to me leaving after so few.

I got in my car and drove to the Hi-Ho Club. It used to be a bootleg spot during prohibition, but changed into a dingy joint over the years. It was a very unhealthy spot for strangers after dark, but I knew the Negro that ran the joint. Four years ago he had backed me up in a little gunplay with a drunken hood and I paid him back a month later by knocking off a punk that tried to set him for a rub-out when he refused to pay off for protection. My name goes pretty strong up that way and since then they let him strictly alone to run his business anyway he pleased. In this racket it's nice to have connections in places like that.

Big Sam was behind the bar. He saw me come in and waved to me with a wet rag over a toothy grin. I shook hands with the guy and ordered a brew. The high yellow and the tall coal black next to me were giving me nasty looks until they heard Big Sam say "Howday, Mistah Hammah. Glad to see yuh. Long time since yuh done been in dis part of town."

When they heard my name mentioned they both moved their drinks six feet down the bar. Sam knew I was here for more than a beer. He moved to the end of the bar and I followed him.

"What's up, Mistah Hammah? Somethin' I can do fuh yuh?"

"Yeah. You got the numbers running in here?"

Sam gave a quick look around before he answered. "Yeah. De boys take 'em down same's they do the othah places. Why?"

"Is George Kalecki still the big boy?"

He licked his thick lips. Sam was nervous. He didn't want to be a squealer, yet he wanted to help me. "It's murder, Sam," I told him. "It's better you tell me than have the bulls drag you to the station. You know how they are."

I could see he was giving it thought. The black skin of his forehead furrowed up. "Okay, Mistah Hammah. Guess it's all right. Kalecki is still head man, but he don't come around hisself. De runners do all the work."

"Is Bobo Hopper doing the running yet? He was with Kalecki some time. Hangs out here all the time, doesn't he?"

"Yassuh. He's head now, but he don' do no mo' running. He done had a good job the last few months. Keeps bees, too."

This was new. Bobo Hopper was only half human, an example of what environment can do to a man. His mental age was about twelve, with a build that went with it. Underfed all his life, he developed into a skinny caricature of a person. I knew him well. A nice Joe that had a heart of gold. No matter how badly you treated him, you were still his friend. Everything was his friend. Birds, animals, insects. Why, once I saw him cry because some kids had stepped on an anthill and crushed a dozen of its occupants. Now he had a "good" job and was keeping bees.

"Where is he, Sam? Back room?"

"Yassuh. You know where. Last I seed him he was looking at a pitcher book of bees."

I polished the beer off in one swallow, hoping the guys that had used it before me didn't have anything contagious. When I passed the high yellow and his friend, I saw their eyes follow me right through the doors of the back room.

Bobo Hopper was sitting at a table in the far corner of the room. The place used to be fixed up with a dice table and a couple of wheels, but now the stuff was stacked in a corner. High up on the wall a single barred window was trying hard to keep out what light seeped down the air shaft, leaving all the work to the solitary bulb dangling on the wire strand from the ceiling. Rubbish was piled high along one side, held back by a few frail pieces of beer poster cardboards.

On the walls a few dirty pictures still hung from thumbtacks, the scenes half wiped out by finger smudges and dust. Someone had tried to copy the stuff in pencil on the wallpaper, but it was a poor try. The door to the bar was the only exit. I fished for the bolt lock, but there was nothing to slide it into so I let it be.

Bobo didn't hear me come in, he was so absorbed in his book. For a few seconds I looked at the pictures over his shoulders, watching his mouth work as he tried to spell out the words. I slammed him on the back.

"Hey, there, don't you say hello to an old friend?"

He half leaped from his chair, then saw that it was me and broke into a big smile. "Gee, Mike Hammer! Golly, I'm glad to see you." He stuck out a skinny paw at me and I took it. "Whatcha doin' down here, Mike? Come down just to see me, huh? Here, lemme get you a chair." He rolled an empty quarter keg that had seen better days over to the table and I parked on it.

"Hear you're keeping bees now, Bobo. That right?"

"Gee, yeah, an' I'm learning all about it from this book here. It's lotsa fun. They even know me, Mike. When I put my hand near the hive they don't bite me at all. They walk on me. You should see them."

"I'll bet it's a lot of fun," I told him. "But bees are expensive to keep, aren't they?"

"Naw. I made the hive from an egg box. And painted it, too. They like their hive. They don't fly away like other guys' do. I got 'em on my roof where the landlady lets me keep 'em. She don't like bees, but I brought her a tiny bit of honey and she liked that. I'm good to my bees."

He was such a nice kid. He bubbled over with enthusiasm. Unlike so many others who were bitter. No family, no home, but now he had a landlady who let him keep bees. Bobo was a funny kid. I couldn't quiz him or he'd clam up, but when you got him talking about something he liked he'd spiel on all day for you.

"I hear you've got a new job, Bobo. How are you making out?"

"Oh, swell, Mike. I like it. They call me the errand manager." They probably meant "erring," but I didn't tell him that.

"What kind of work it is?" I asked. "Very hard?"

"Uh-uh. I run errands and deliver things and sweep and everything. Sometimes Mr. Didson lets me ride his bicycle when I deliver things for his store. I have lots of fun. Meet nice people, too."

"Do you make much money?"

"Sure. I get most a quarter or a half buck every time I do something. Them Park Avenue swells like me. Last week I made nearly fifteen bucks." Fifteen bucks. That was a lot of dough to him. He lived simply enough; now he was proud of himself. So was I.

"Sounds pretty good, Bobo. How did you ever manage to run down such a good job?"

"Well, you remember old Humpy?" I nodded. Humpy was a hunchback in his late forties who shined shoes in Park Avenue offices. I used him for an eye several times. He'd do anything to make a buck.

"Old Humpy got T.B.," Bobo continued. "He went up in the mountains to shine shoes there and I took his place. Only I wasn't so good at it like him. Then folks asked me to do little things for them and I did. Now I go down there every day early in the morning and the give me things to do like running errands. I got a day off today on account of I gotta see a guy about buying a queen bee. He's got two. Do you think five bucks is too much to pay for a queen bee, Mike?"

"Oh, I don't think so." I didn't know a queen bee from a king cobra, but queens usually run high in any species. "What did Mr. Kalecki say when you quit running numbers for him?"

Bobo didn't clam up like I expected. "Gee, he was swell. Gimme ten bucks 'cause I was with him so long and told me I could have my old job back whenever I wanted it." No wonder. Bobo was as honest as the day was long. Generally a runner made plenty for himself, taking a chance that the dough he clipped wasn't on the number that pulled in the shekels. But Bobo was too simple to be dishonest.

"That was pretty nice of Mr. Kalecki," I grinned, "but you do better when you're in business for yourself."

"Yeah. Some day I'm just gonna raise bees. You can make a lot of money from bees. Even own a bee farm, maybe."

Bobo smiled happily at the thought of it. But his smile passed into a puzzled frown. His eyes were fastened on something behind me. I had my back to the door, but when I saw Bobo's face, I knew that we weren't alone in the back room any longer.

The knife went under my chin very slowly. It was held loosely enough, but the slim fingers that held it were ready to tighten up the second I moved. Along the blade were the marks of a whetstone, so I knew it had been sharpened recently. The forefinger was laid on the top of the four-inch blade in proper cutting position. Here was a lug that knew what it was all about.

Bobo's eyes were wide open with terror. His mouth worked, but no sound came from it. The poor kid began to sweat, little beads that ran in rivulets down his sallow cheeks. A brown-sleeved arm came over my other shoulder and slid nicely under my coat lapel, the hand reaching for my rod.

I clamped down and kicked back. The table went sailing as my feet caught it. I got the knife hand and pulled down hard, and the high yellow landed in a heap on top of me. Just in time I saw the foot coming and pulled my head aside. The coal black missed by inches. I didn't. I let go the knife hand and grabbed the leg. The next moment I was fighting for my life under two sweating Negroes.

But not for long. The knife came out again and this time I got the hand in a wristlock and twisted. The tendons stretched, and the bones snapped sickeningly. The high yellow let out a scream and dropped the knife. I was on my feet in a flash. The big black buck was up and came charging into me, his head down.

There was no sense to busting my hand on his skull, so I lashed out with my foot and the toe of my shoe caught the guy right in the face. He toppled over sideways, still running, and collapsed against the wall. His lower teeth were protruding through his lip. Two of his incisors were lying beside his nose, plastered there with blood.

The high yellow was holding his broken wrist in one hand, trying to get to his feet. I helped him. My hand hooked in his collar and dragged him up. I took the side of my free hand and smashed it across his nose. The bone shattered and blood poured out. That guy probably was a lady killer in Harlem, but them days were gone forever. He let out a little moan and slumped to the floor. I let him drop.

Just for the hell of it, I went through his pockets. Not much there. A cheap wallet held a few photos of girls, one of them white, eleven dollars and a flock of number stubs. The coal black covered his ruined face when I went near him, rolling his eyes like a cow. I found a safety-razor blade in his pocket with a matchstick through it. Nice trick. They palm the blade, letting it protrude a bit through the fingers, and slap you cross the face. The matchstick keeps it from sliding through their fingers. That blade can cut a face to pieces.

The Negro tried to pull away, so I smashed him again. The pad of my fist landing on that busted jaw was too much for him. He went out too. Bobo was still in his chair, only now he was grinning again. "Gee, Mike, you're pretty tough. Wish I was like that."

I pulled a five spot from my pocket and slipped it in his shirt pocket. "Here's something to buy a king for that queen bee, kid," I said to him. "See you later." I grabbed the two jigs by their collars and yanked them out of the door. Big Sam saw me coming with them. So did a dozen others in the place. Those at the door looked like they expected something more.

"What's the idea, Sam? Why let these monkeys make a try for me? You know better than that."

Big Sam just grinned broader than ever. "It's been a long time since we had some excitements in here, Mistah Hammah." He turned to the guys at the bar and held out a thick palm. "Pay me," he laughed at them. I dropped the high yellow and his friend in a heap on the floor as the guys paid Sam off. The next time they wouldn't bet against me.

As I was waving so long to Sam, Bobo came running out of the back room waving the five. "Hey, Mike," he yelled. "Queens don't need no kings. I can't buy a king bee."

"Sure they do, Bobo," I called over my shoulder. "All queens have to have kings. Ask Sam there, he'll tell you." Bobo was trying to find out why from Sam when I left. He'd probably spend the rest of his life getting the answer.

The drive home took longer than I had expected. Traffic was heavy and it was nearly six when I got there. After I parked the car I took the stairs to my apartment and started to undress. My clean shirt was a mess. Blood was spattered all over the front of it and my tie was halfway around my neck. The pocket of my jacket was ripped down the seam. When I saw that I wished I'd killed that bogie. In these days decent suits were too hard to get.

A hot and cold shower made me feel fine. I got rid of my beard in short order, brushed my teeth and climbed into some fresh clothes. For a moment I wondered whether it would be decent to wear a gun when calling on a lady, but habit got the better of me. I slipped the holster on over my shirt, shot a few drops of oil in the slide mechanism of my .45 and checked my clip. Everything in order, I wiped the gun and shoved it under my arm. Anyway, I thought, my suit wouldn't fit unless old ironsides was inside it. This was a custom-made job that had space built into it for some artillery.

I checked myself in the mirror to be sure I hadn't forgotten anything. Without Velda to give me a once-over before I went anywhere, I couldn't tell whether I was dolled up for a circus or a night club. Now I wished I had been more careful with the Bellemy mouse. Velda was too good a woman to lose. Guess I could expect the silent treatment for a week. Someday I'd have to try treating her a little better. She was kind of hard on a guy though, never approved of my morals.

The jalopy needed gas so I ran it into a garage. Henry, the mechanic, and an old friend of mine, lifted the hood to check the oil. He liked that car. He was the one who installed an oversized engine in it and pigged down the frame. From the outside it looked like any beat-up wreck that ought to be retired, but the rubber was good and the engine better. It was souped up to the ears. I've had it on the road doing over a hundred and the pedal was only half down. Henry pulled the motor from a limousine that had the rear end knocked in and sold it to me for a song. Whenever a mech saw the power that was under the hood, he let out a long low whistle. In is own way it was a masterpiece.

I pulled out of the garage and turned down a one-way street to beat the lights to Charlotte's apartment. I couldn't forget the way she looked through me the last time we met. What a dish.

The road in front of her house was lined with cars, so I turned around the block and slid in between a black sedan and a club coupé. Walking back to her place I kept hoping she didn't have a dinner date or any company. That would be just my luck. What we would talk about was something else again. In the back of my mind was the idea that as a psychiatrist, she would have been more observant than any of the others. In her line it was details that counted, too.

I rang the downstairs bell. A moment later the buzzer clicked and I walked in. The darky maid was at the door to greet me, but this time she had on her hat and coat.

"Come right in, Mistah Hammah," she said, "Miss Charlotte's expecting ya'll." At that I really raised my eyebrows. I threw my hat down on a table beside the door and walked in. The maid stayed long enough to call into the bedroom, "He's heah, Miss Charlotte."

That cool voice called back. "Thank you. You can go ahead to the movies now." I nodded to the darky as she left and sat on the couch.

"Hello." I jumped to my feet and took the warm hand she offered me.

"Hello yourself," I smiled, "What's this about expecting me?"

"I'm just vain, I guess. I was hoping so hard that you'd call tonight. I got ready for you. Like my dress?" She swirled in front of me, and glanced over her shoulder at my face. Gone was the psychiatrist. Here was Charlotte Manning, the woman, looking delightfully young and beautiful. Her dress was a tight-fitting blue silk jersey that clung to her like she was wet, concealing everything, yet revealing everything. Her hair hung long and yellow to her neck, little tight curls that sparkled. Even her eyes had cupids in them.

She strode provocatively across the room and back toward me. Under the dress her body was superb, unlike what I imagined the first time. She was slimmer, really, her waist thin, but her shoulders broad. Her breasts were laughing things that were firmly in place, although I could see no strap marks of a restraining bra. Her legs were encased in sheer nylons and set in high heels, making her almost as tall as I was. Beautiful legs. They were strong-looking, shapely. . . .

"Well, do you like it?" she asked again.

"Lovely. And you know it." I grinned at her. "You remind me of something."

"What?"

"A way of torturing a guy."

"Oh, please, I can't be that bad. Do I affect you like that? Torture you, I mean?"

"No, not quite. But if you take a guy that hasn't seen a woman in five years, let's say, and chain him to a wall and let you walk past him the way you did just now—well, that would be torture. See what I'm getting at?"

Her laugh was low and throaty. She threw back her head a little and I wanted to grab her and kiss the beauty of her throat. Charlotte took my arm and led me to the kitchen. The table was laid out for two. On the table was a big pile of fried chicken and another equally large basket of french fries.

"Just for us. Now sit down and eat. I've already held supper an hour waiting for you."

I was dumbfounded. Either she kept a complete file of my likes and dislikes or she was clairvoyant. Chicken was my specialty.

As I pulled out a chair and sat down, I said, "Charlotte, if there was an angle to this, I'd think the chow was poisoned. But even if it is, I'm going to eat it anyway."

She was putting a red-bordered apron on. When she finished she poured the coffee. "There is an angle," she said casually.

"Let's have it," I said through a mouthful of chicken.

"When you came in to see me I saw a man that I liked for the first time in a long time." She sat down and continued. "I have hundreds of patients, and surprisingly enough, most of them are men. But they are such little men. Either they had no character to begin with or what they had is gone. Their minds are frail, their conception limited. So many have repressions or obsessions, and they come to me with their pitiful stories; well, when you constantly see men with their masculinity gone, and find the same sort among those whom you call your friends, you get so you actually search for a real man."

"Thanks," I put in.

"No, I mean it," Charlotte went on. "I diagnosed you the moment you set foot in my office. I saw a man who was used to living and could make life obey the rules he set down. Your body is huge, your mind is the same. No repressions."

I wiped my mouth. "I got an obsession though."

"You have? I can't imagine what it is."

"I want a killer. I want to shoot a killer." I watched her over a drumstick, chewing a mile a minute on the succulent dark meat. She tossed her hair and nodded.

"Yes, but it's a worthwhile obsession. Now eat up."

I went through the pile of chicken in nothing flat. My plate was heaped high with bones. Charlotte did all right, too, but I did most of the damage. After a piece of pie and a second cup of coffee I leaned back in my chair, contented as a cow.

"That's a wonderful cook you've got there," I remarked.

"Cook, hell," she laughed. "I did all that myself. I haven't always been wealthy."

"Well, when the time comes for you to get married, you're not going to have to go out of your way to get a husband."

"Oh, I have a system," she said. "You're getting part of it right now. I lure men to my apartment, cook for them, and before they go home I have my proposal."

"Don't look now," I told her, "but it's been tried on me before."

"But not by an expert." We both laughed at that. I suggested we do the dishes and she handed me an apron. Very politely, I laid it on the back of a chair. It just wouldn't go well with my mug. If anyone I knew happened to breeze in and catch me in a rig like that I'd spend the rest of my life living it down.

After we finished the dishes we went into the living room. Charlotte curled up in the armchair and I half fell onto the sofa.

We lit cigarettes, then she smiled at me and said, "All right, you can tell me why you came up to see me. More questions?"

I shook my head. "I confess. Don't beat me with that whip. I started out with two things in mind. The first one was to see you with your hair down. It turned out better than I expected."

"And the other?"

"To see if you, as a practicing psychiatrist, could throw some light on the murder of my good friend, Jack Williams."

"I see. Perhaps if you tell me more explicitly what you want, I'll be able to help you."

"Good enough. I want details. The murder isn't old enough to get well into it yet, but I will. It's entirely reasonable that someone at the party knocked off Jack. It's just as reasonable that it was someone completely outside. I've made some character studies, and what I've found I don't like. However, that may not be a good reason for murder. What I want from you is an opinion, not one based on fact or logic, but an opinion, purely professional, on how you think those I mentioned may tie into this thing and whom you'd line up for the killer."

Charlotte took a deep drag on her cigarette, then crushed it out in an ashtray. Her mind was working hard, it was reflected in her expression. A minute passed before she spoke. "You are asking me to do a difficult thing, pass judgment on a person. Usually it takes twelve men and a judge, after hours of deliberation, to do the same thing. Mike, after I met you, I made it my job to look into your character. I wanted to know what a man like you was made of. It wasn't hard to find out. The papers have been full of your episodes, editorials were even written about you, and not very favorable ones, either. Yet I found people who knew you and liked you. Little people and big people. I like you. But if I were to tell you what I thought I'm afraid I'd be passing a sentence of death on a person. No, I won't tell you that, you'd be too quick to kill. That I don't want. There's so much about you that could be nice if only your mind wasn't trained to hate too fiercely.

"What I will do is give you that which I have observed. It takes time to think back, and I've taken the whole afternoon to do just that. Little things I thought I had forgotten are clear now and they may make sense to you. I'm used to personal conflict, the struggle that goes on within one's mind, not with differences between two or more people. I can notice things, put them in their proper places, but I can't do more than file them away. If a person hates, then I can find the reason for his hatred and possibly help him to rationalize more clearly, but if that hatred has consumed him to the point of murder, then I can but say I might have expected it. The discovery of murderers and motives belongs to more astute minds than mine."

I was listening intently to every word, and I could see her point. "Fair enough," I said, "then tell me what you have observed."

"It isn't too much. Jack had been in a state of nervous tension for a week before the party. I saw him twice and neither time had he seemed any better. I remarked about it, but he laughed and told me he was still trying to rehabilitate himself to civilian life. At the time it seemed reasonable to me. A man who has lost a limb would naturally find life awkward for some time.

"The night of the party he was still as tense as ever. Somehow, it radiated to Myrna. She worried about him anyway, and I could see that she was nearly as upset as he was. Nothing visible, however, just those little things. A tendency to anger at the dropping of a glass or a sudden sound. Both Jack and she covered it up nicely, so I imagine that I was the only one who noticed anything.

"Mr. Kalecki came to the party in a grouch. Perhaps anger would be a better word, but I couldn't figure out with whom he was angry. He snapped at Harold Kines several times and was completely uncivil to Mary Bellemy."

"How?" I asked.

"They were dancing and she said something or other. I didn't hear what it was, but he scowled and said, 'The hell with that stuff, sister.' Right after that he took her back to the group and walked away."

I laughed. She didn't know what was so funny until I told her. "Mary Bellemy probably propositioned George right on the floor. Guess he's getting old. She's a nymphomaniac."

"Oh, yes? How did you find out?" The way she said it was with icebergs.

"Don't get ideas," I said. "She tried it on me but I wasn't in the market."

"Right then?"

"No, never. I like to do some of the work myself, not have it handed to me on a platter."

"I'll have to remember that. I did suspect that Mary was like that, but I never gave it much thought. We were only casual friends. Anyway, when we were leaving, Jack stopped me by the door and asked me to stop back to see him sometime during the week. Before he could say anything further, the gang called me and I had to leave. I never saw him again."

"I see." I tried to mull it over in my mind, but it didn't work out. So Jack had something bothering him, and so did Myrna. It might have been that they were worried about the same thing. Maybe not. And George. He was upset about something, too.

"What do you make of it?" Charlotte asked.

"Nothing, but I'll think it over." Charlotte got up from the chair and came over to the sofa and sat down. She laid her hand on mine and our eyes met.

"Mike, do me a favor. I'm not asking you to stay out of this and let the police handle it, all I want is for you to be careful. Please don't get hurt."

When she spoke like that I felt as if I had known her a lifetime. Her hand was warm and pulsing lightly. I felt myself going fast— and I had seen her only twice.

"I'll be careful," I told her. "Why are you worrying?"

"Here's why." She leaned forward, her lips parted, and kissed me on the mouth. I squeezed her arms so hard my hands hurt, but she never moved. When she drew away her eyes were soft and shining. Inside me a volcano was blazing. Charlotte looked at the marks on her arms where I held her and smiled.

"You love hard, too, don't you, Mike?"

This time I didn't hurt her. I stood up and drew her toward me. I pressed her to me, closely, so she could feel the fire I had in me. This kiss lasted longer. It was a kiss I'll never forget. Then I kissed her eyes, and that spot on her throat that looked so delicious. It was better than I expected.

I turned her around and we faced the windows overlooking the street. She rubbed her head against mine, holding my arms around her waist tightly. "I'm going now," I said to her. "If I don't, I'll never leave. The next time I'll stay longer. I don't want to do this wrong. I will if you keep me here."

She tilted her head up and I kissed her nose. "I understand," she said softly. "But whenever you want me, I'll be here. Just come and get me."

I kissed her again, lightly this time, then went to the door. She handed me my hat and pushed my hair back for me. "Good-bye, Mike."

I winked at her. "So long, Charlotte. It was a wonderful supper with a wonderful girl."

It was a wonder I got downstairs at all. I hardly remember getting to my car. All I could think of was her face and that lovely body. The way she kissed and the intensity in her eyes. I stopped on Broadway and dropped into a bar for a drink to clear my head. It didn't help so I went home and hit the sack earlier than usual.

chapter 7

I WOKE up before the alarm went off, which is pretty unusual. After a quick shower and shave, I whipped up some scrambled eggs and shoveled them into me. When I was on my second cup of coffee the boy from the tailor shop came in with my suit nicely cleaned and pressed. The pocket was sewed up so that you could never have told it was torn. I dressed leisurely and called the office.

"Hammer Investigating Agency, good morning."

"Good morning yourself, Velda, this is your boss."

"Oh."

"Aw, come on, honey," I pleaded, "quit being sore at me. That lipstick came under the line of business. How can I work when you've got me by the neck?"

"You seem to do all right," her reply came back. "What can I do for you, *Mister* Hammer?"

"Any calls?"

"Nope."

"Any mail?"

"Nope."

"Anybody been in?"

"Nope."

"Will you marry me?"

"Nope."

"Well, so long then."

"Marry? Hey . . . wait a minute, Mike. MIKE! Hello . . . hello. . . ."

I hung up very gently, laughing to myself. That would fix her. The next time she'd do more than say "nope." I'd better start watching that stuff. Can't afford to trip myself up; though with Velda maybe it wouldn't be so bad at that.

The police had taken their watchdog away from Jack's apartment. The door was still sealed pending further investigation and I didn't want to get in dutch with the D.A.'s office by breaking it, so I looked around a bit.

I had just about given up when I remembered that the bathroom window bordered on an air shaft, and directly opposite it was another window. I walked around the hall and knocked on a door. A small, middle-aged gent poked his head out and I flashed my badge on him. "Police," was all I had to say.

He didn't bother looking the badge over, but opened the door

in haste. A good respectable citizen that believed in law and order. He stood in front of me, clutching a worn smoking jacket
around his pot belly and trying to look innocent. Right then he
was probably thinking of some red light he ran a month ago, and
picturing himself in the line-up.

"Er . . . yes, officer, what can I do for you?"

"I'm investigating possible entries into the apartment of Mr.
Williams. I understand you have a window that faces his. Is that
right?"

His jaw dropped. "Wh-why, yes, but nobody could have gone
through our window without us seeing him."

"That isn't the point," I explained to him. "Somebody could
have come down from the roof on a rope. What I want to do is
see if that window can be opened from the outside. And I don't
want to shinny down a rope to do it."

The guy sighed with relief. "Oh, I see. Well, of course, just
come this way." A mousey-type woman stuck her head from the
bedroom door and asked, "John, what is it?"

"Police," he told her importantly. "They want me to help
them." He led me to the bathroom and I pushed up the window.
It was some job. Those modest folks, fearing somebody might
peek, must never have had it open. When it went up, a shower of
paint splinters fluttered to the floor.

There was Jack's bathroom window, all right. A space of three
feet separated the two walls. I worked myself to the outside sill
while the little guy held my belt to steady me. Then I let myself
fall forward. The guy let out a shriek and his wife came tearing in.
But all I did was stick my hands out and lean against the opposite
wall. He thought I was a goner.

The bathroom window went up easily. I pulled myself across the space, thanked the guy and his wife, and slithered inside. Nothing had been moved around much. The fingerprint crew had left powder tracings on most of the objects that could have been handled, and where Jack's body had lain were the chalk marks outlining the position. His artificial arm was still on the bed where he had put it. The only thing that was gone was his gun, and stuck in the empty holster was a note. I pulled it out and read it. "Mike," it said, "don't get excited over the gun. I have it at headquarters." It was signed, "Pat."

How do you like that? He thought I'd find a way to get in. I put the note back with an addition at the bottom. "Thanks, chum," I wrote, "I won't." I scrawled my name underneath it.

It was easy to see that the police had been over everything in the place. They had gone at it neatly, but completely. Everything was replaced much the same as it had been. There were just a few things not quite in order that made it possible to tell that it had been searched.

I started in the living room. After I pushed the chairs to the middle of the floor and examined them, I went around the edges of the carpet. Nothing there but a little dirt. I found three cents under the cushions of the couch, but that was all. The insides of the radio hadn't been touched for months, as evidenced by the dust that had settled there. What books were around had nothing in them, no envelopes, no bookmarks or paper of any sort. If they had, the police got them.

When I finished, I replaced everything and tried the bathroom but, except for the usual array of bottles and shaving things in the cabinet, it was empty.

The bedroom was next. I lifted the mattress and felt along the seams for any possible opening or place where it may have been stitched up. I could have cursed my luck. I stood in the middle of the floor stroking my chin, thinking back. Jack had kept a diary, but he kept it on his dresser. It wasn't there now. The police again. I even tried the window shades, thinking that a paper might have been rolled up in one of them.

What got me was that I knew Jack had kept a little pad of notes and addresses ever since he was on the force. If I could find that, it might contain something useful. I tried the dresser. I took every shirt, sock and set of underwear out of the drawers and went through them, but I might as well not have taken the time. Nothing.

As I emptied the bottom drawer a tie caught and slipped over the back. I pulled the drawer all the way out and picked up the tie from the plywood bottom. I also picked up something else. I picked up Jack's little book.

I didn't want to go through it right then. It was nearly ten o'clock and there was a chance that either the police might walk in on me or the little guy get suspicious enough of my being away so long he'd call a copper. As quickly as I could, I put the stuff back in the drawers and replaced them in the dresser. The book I stuck in my hip pocket.

The little guy was waiting for me in his own bathroom. I squeezed out Jack's window and made a pretense of looking for rope marks along the upper sill. His eyes followed me carefully. "Find anything, Officer?" he asked me.

"Afraid not. No marks around here at all. I checked the other windows and they haven't even been opened." I tried to look up to the roof, but I couldn't get back far enough until I stepped across to his side, then I wormed my way into the bathroom and poked my head out and craned my head to make it look like I was really trying.

"Well, I guess that's all. Might as well go out through your door as climb back inside there, okay?"

"Certainly, Officer, right this way." He steered me to the front room like a seeing-eye dog and opened up for me. "Any time we can be of service, Officer," he called to me as I left, "let us know. Glad to help."

I drove back to the office in short order and walked into the reception room, pulling the book from my pocket. Velda stopped typing. "Mike."

I turned around. I knew what was coming.

"What is it, honey?"

"Please don't fool with me like that."

I gave her a big grin. "I wasn't fooling," I said. "If you were on your toes I'd be an engaged man right now. Come on inside a minute." She trailed in after me and sat down. I swung my feet up on the battered desk and riffled through the book. Velda was interested.

"What is it?" she asked curiously, leaning over to get a better look.

"A notebook of Jack's. I swiped it from his room before the police could get it."

"Anything in it?"

"Maybe. I haven't looked yet." Starting at the front was a list of names, all crossed out. Each page was dated, the earliest starting three years ago. Occasionally there were references to departmental cases with possible suspects and the action to take. These, too, were crossed out as having been completed.

About the middle of the book notes began to appear that apparently were still active or pending, for no black X's marked them. I jotted these down on a list and Velda checked them against news clippings in my files. When she finished she laid down my notes with the word "solved" after each. Evidently the cases had been cleared up while Jack was still in the army.

I wasn't getting much at all from this. Jack had inserted a single page with one word across it. "WHOOPIE!" It was dated the day of his discharge. The next page had a recipe for veal paprika, and at the bottom was a notation to put more salt in than the recipe called for.

There were two more pages of figures, an itemized account of what he had spent for clothes balanced against what he had in a bank account somewhere. Then came a brief remark: "Eileen Vickers. Family still in Poughkeepsie."

She must have been a girl from home. Jack was born in Poughkeepsie and lived there until he went to college. The next few pages had some instructions from the insurance company. Then Eileen Vickers' name cropped up again. This time it read: "Saw E. V. again. Call family." The date was exactly two weeks before Jack had been killed.

She turned up again five pages further on. In heavy pencil Jack had: "R. H. Vickers, c/o Halper. Pough. 221. Call after 6." Then below it: "E. V. al. Mary Wright. No address. Get it later."

I tried to puzzle out what it meant. To me it looked like Jack had met a girl from home and had talked to her. She had told him that her family was still in Poughkeepsie. Evidently he tried to call them and found that they were staying with Halper, and in order to get them, called at suppertime. Then the next part. E. V., Eileen Vickers, all right, but she was traveling under an alias of Mary Wright and gave no address.

I thumbed through the pages quickly, and there she was again. "E. V. Call family. Bad shape. Trace and raid 36904 the 29th." And today was the 29th. There was one page left. It was an afterthought, a memo to himself: "Ask C. M. what she can do."

C. M., Charlotte Manning. He had reference to what Charlotte told me about. He wanted her to stop back during the week, but never got the chance to see her.

I reached for the phone and dialed operator. When she cut in I asked for the Poughkeepsie number. There were some clicks as the connection was completed, then a timid voice answered.

"Hello," I said. "Is this Mr. Vickers?"

"No," the voice replied, "this is Mr. Halper. Mr. Vickers is still at work. Can you leave a message?"

"Well, I wanted to find out if he had a daughter in the city. Do you know—"

The voice interrupted me. "I'm sorry, but it would be better if you didn't mention that to Mr. Vickers. Who is calling, please?"

"This is Michael Hammer, investigator. I'm working with the police on a murder and I'm trying to run down what might be a lead. Now, can you tell me what the story is here?"

Halper hesitated a moment, then said, "Very well. Mr. Vickers hasn't seen his daughter since she went to college. She became enmeshed in a sinful life with a young man. Mr. Vickers is a very stern gentleman, and as far as he is concerned, she might as well be dead. He'll have nothing to do with her."

"I see, thank you." I hung up and turned to Velda. She was staring at the number I had jotted down. 36904.

"Mike."

"What?"

"Do you know what this is?" I looked at the number. It could have been a reference to a police file, but when I glanced at it a third time, I felt as though I had seen it before.

"Uh-uh. I should know it, I think. Something vaguely familiar about it."

Velda took a pencil from her pocket and swung the pad around. "Suppose you write it this way," she said. She put the numbers down to read: XX3-6904.

"Well, I'll be damned! A phone number."

"Roger, pal. Now fill in the first two letters of an exchange for the X's and you'll have it."

I jumped to my feet and went to the files. Now I remembered where I had seen that number before. It was on the back of a card I had taken from a pimp. The little runt had tried to sell me a deal and I slapped him silly for it. I came back with a folder of note paper, cards, and numbers, scratched on the back of menus.

I picked one out of the file. "LEARN TO DANCE" it read, "TWENTY BEAUTIFUL GIRLS." On the back of it was a number. I compared it to the one from Jack's book. The same. Only this one had an exchange, LO, for Loellen. That was the number, all right, LO3-6904. Velda took it from my hand and read it.

"What is it, Mike?"

"It's the telephone number of a call house. If I'm not mistaken, that's where I'm going to find the Vickers girl." I reached for the phone, but Velda put her hand out to stop me.

"You're not actually going there, are you?"

"Why not?"

"Mike!" Her voice was indignant, hurt.

"For Pete's sake, honey, do I look like a dope? I'm not going to buy anything. After all those pictures the army showed me of what happens to good little boys who go out with bad little girls, I'm even afraid to kiss my own mother."

"Okay, go ahead, but watch your step, by damn, or you're going to have to get a new secretary." I ran my fingers through her hair and dialed the number.

The voice I got this time had a little life in it. Behind the "hello" I could see a frowsy blonde about fifty in a gaudy dress dangling a butt from her lips.

"Hello," I said, "you booked for the night?"

"Who is this?"

"Pete Sterling. Got your number from a little guy downtown."

"All right. Come up before nine or you won't make the beginning of the entertainment. Want to stay all night?"

"Maybe. I'll know better then. Book me for the night anyway. Guess I can get away from home." I winked at Velda when I said it, but she didn't wink back.

"You're down. Bring cash. Ring three longs and a short when you come."

"I got it." I cradled the phone.

There were tears in Velda's eyes. She was trying to remain grim, but she couldn't hold them back.

I put my arms around her and hugged her gently. "Aw, look, honey," I whispered, "I have to take a realistic approach to this case. Otherwise, how the hell am I going to get anywhere?"

"You don't have to go that far," she sniffled.

"But I told you I wouldn't. For crying out loud, I'm not that bad off that I have to patronize those places. There's lots of dames I could park with if I felt like it."

She put her hands against my chest and shoved. "And don't I know it," she practically yelled. "I wouldn't trust you to . . . oh, gee, Mike, I'm sorry. I only work here. Forget it."

I pinched her nose and smiled. "Work here, hell. I wouldn't know what to do without you. Now behave yourself and stick near your phone either here or at home. I may need you to pick up a few angles for me."

Velda gave a little laugh. "Okay, Mike. I'll watch the angles, you watch out for the curves. Huba huba."

She was cleaning off my desk when I left.

chapter

8

My first call was to Pat. He wanted to know how I was making out but I didn't give him much. Later he could know about the Vickers girl, but first I wanted to get in my two bits. I picked a few numbers from the phone book and included the call-house number among them. I held on while Pat checked the addresses for me and passed on the information. After I thanked him, I checked with the phone book to make sure he had given me straight stuff. They checked. Pat was playing it square enough.

In case he fished around with the numbers I gave him, it would be some time before he got to the one I was working on.

This time I left my heap halfway down the block. Five oh one was the number I wanted, and it turned out to be an old brownstone apartment three stories high. I cased it from a spot across the street, but no one came or went. On the top floor a room was lit up faintly with no signs of life in it. Evidently I was early. The house was flanked on each side by another equally as drab and with as little color to it as the streets of a ghost town.

This was no regular red-light district. Just a good spot for what went on. An old, quiet neighborhood patrolled several times nightly by a friendly cop, a few struggling businesses in the basement apartments. No kids—the street was too dull for them. No drunks lounging in doorways either. I pulled on my cigarette for the last time, then crushed it under my heel and started across the street.

I pushed the button three longs and a short. Very faintly I heard the ring, then the door opened. It wasn't the frowsy blonde I had expected. This woman was about fifty, all right, but her dress was conservative and neat. She had her hair done up in a roll with only the slightest suggestion of makeup. She looked like somebody's mother.

"Pete Sterling," I said.

"Oh, yes, won't you come in?" She closed the door behind me while I waited, then motioned toward the sitting room off the hall. I went in. The transformation was startling. Unlike the dull exterior, this room was exciting, alive. The furniture was modern, yet comfortable. The walls were paneled in rich mahogany to blend with the redecorated mantel and the graceful staircase that curved down into the far end of the room. I could see why no light shone through the windows. They were completely blocked off with black velvet curtains.

"May I take your hat?" I snapped out of it long enough to hand over my lid. Upstairs a radio was playing, but there was no other sound. The woman came back after a moment and sat down, motioning me to be seated opposite her.

"Nice place you have," I remarked.

"Yes, we're very secluded here." I was waiting for her to ask the questions, but she seemed in no hurry. "You told me on the phone that you had met one of our agents and he sent you here. Which one was it?"

"A little ratty guy. He didn't make it sound as good as this. I slapped him around some."

She gave me a tight smile. "Yes, I remember, Mr. Hammer. He had to take the week off." If she thought she'd catch me jumping she was crazy.

"How did you spot me?"

"Please don't be so modest. You've made too many headlines to be entirely unknown. Now tell me something, why did you choose to come here?"

"Guess," I said.

She smiled again. "I imagine it can even happen to you, too. All right, Mr. . . . er . . . Sterling, would you like to go upstairs?"

"Yeah. Who's up there?"

"An assortment you'll find interesting. You'll see. But first, twenty-five dollars, please." I fished out the dough and handed it over.

She led me as far as the stairs. There was a push button mounted on the side of the newel post and she pushed it. Upstairs a chime rang and a door opened, flooding the stairs with light. A dark-haired girl wrapped in a transparent robe stood in the doorway.

"Come on up," she said.

I took the stairs two at a time. She wasn't pretty, I could see that, but the makeup enhanced what she had. A beautiful body, though. I walked in. Another sitting room, but this one was well occupied. The madam had meant what she said when she told me there was an assortment. The girls were sitting there reading or smoking; blondes, brunettes and a pair of redheads. None of them had much on.

Things like this were supposed to make your heart beat faster, only I didn't react that way. I thought of Velda and Jack. Something was here that I wanted and I didn't know how I was going to take it. Eileen Vickers was the one, but I never saw her. The alias—Mary Wright. It seemed feasible that she would not use her right name working here and not to evade income taxes either.

Nobody gave me a tumble, so I supposed I was to make the selection. The girl who led me in kept watching me expectantly. "Want someone special?" she asked.

"Mary Wright," I told her.

"She's in her room. Wait here, I'll get her." The girl disappeared through the door and was back a moment later. "Right down the hall, next to last door."

I nodded and went through the door and found myself in a long hallway. On either side the wall was peppered with doors, newly built. Each one had a knob, but no keyhole. The next to last door was the same as the others. I knocked and a voice called out for me to come in. I turned the knob and pushed.

Mary Wright was seated in front of a dressing table, combing her hair. All she was wearing was a brassiére and a pair of step-ins. That and house slippers. She eyed me through the mirror.

She might have been pretty once, but she wasn't any longer. There were lines under her eyes that weren't put there by age. She had a faint twitch in her cheek that she tried to conceal, but it came through anyway. I guessed her age somewhat in the late twenties. She looked a lot older, but I accounted for that.

Here was a girl that had seen plenty of life, all raw. Her body was just a shade too thin, well fed, but emotionally starved. Empty, like a dead snail. Her profession and her past were etched into her eyes. She was a girl you could beat without getting a whimper out of her. Maybe her expression would change, but another beating more or less would mean nothing. Like the others, she wasn't too made up. Far from being plain, but not at all gaudy.

Her hair was a chestnut brown like the irises of her eyes. She must have had some sun lately or spent time under a lamp, for there was a faint tinge of tan covering what I could see of her skin. There was nothing startling about her shape. Average. Not very heavy in the breasts, but her legs were nice. I felt sorry for the girl.

"Hello." Her voice was pleasant enough. She sat there as though she was getting ready to go out and I was a husband casually looking for a cuff link. "Early, aren't you?"

"Sort of, but I was getting tired of hanging around a bar." I got in a quick look around the room, then went to an end table and ran through a set of books. My fingers felt under the table edge before I inspected the walls. I was looking for wires. These places have been rigged for sound more than once and I didn't want to get snared in a trap. The bed was next. I got down on my hands and knees and looked under it. No wires.

Mary had been watching me curiously. "If it's a dictaphone you're searching for, we haven't any," she said. "And the walls are soundproofed besides." She stood up in front of me. "Want a drink first?"

"No."

"Afterwards, then."

"No."

"Why?"

"Because I didn't come here for that."

"Well, for goodness' sake, what did you come for, to make small talk?"

"You hit it, Eileen." I thought she'd pass out. At first she got deathly white, then her eyes hardened and her lips tightened. I could see that this wasn't going to be so easy.

"What's the gag, mister? Who are you?"

"The monicker is Mike Hammer, kid. I'm a private eye."

She knew who I was all right. She tightened up all over when she heard my name. A traceless fear crept into her body. "So you're a shamus. What does that have to do with me? If my father sent you—"

I cut her short. "Your father didn't send me. Nobody did. A pal of mine got killed a short time ago. His name was Jack Williams." Her hand flew to her mouth. For a second I thought she'd scream. But she didn't. She sat down on the edge of the bed, and a tear trickled down her cheek leaving a streak in the makeup.

"No. I—I didn't know."

"Don't you read the papers?" She shook her head. "Among his things I found your name. He'd seen you just before, hadn't he?"

"Yes. Please, am I under arrest?"

"No. I don't want to arrest anybody. I just want to shoot some-body. The killer." The tears were coming freely now. She tried to wipe them away but they came too fast.

It was hard to understand. Here was a dame I had tagged as being as hard as they come, yet she thought enough of Jack to cry when I told her he was dead. And she hated her father, apparently. Well, that was a woman. There was still that much left in her.

"Not Jack. He was so nice. I—I really tried to keep this from him, but he found out. He even got me a job before, but I couldn't keep it." Mary rolled over on her face and buried her head in the pillow. She was sobbing hard now.

I sat down next to her. "Crying won't help. What I want are a few answers. Come on, sit up and listen." I raised her by the shoulders. "Jack wanted to have this place raided tonight, but the message never reached the police. He was killed before he could do anything about it. What's going on tonight?"

Mary straightened up. Her tears were gone now and she was thinking. I had to let her take her time. "I don't know," she said finally. "Jack had no cause to do anything. Places like this flourish in the city and they don't have to pay off to anyone."

"Maybe there's more to it than you think," I added. "Just who is expected tonight?"

She continued, "The show. Lots of people come to see it. You know the kind. Usually there's a convention in town and prospective buyers are brought here for a little fun. I never see any important people. The kind that are in the public eye, I mean. Just fairly prosperous people."

I knew the kind. Fat greasy people from out of town. Slick city boys who played the angles and were willing to shell out the dough. Rich jokers of both sexes who liked smut and filth and didn't care where they got it. A pack of queers who enjoyed exotic, sadistic sex. Nasty people. Clerks who scraped their nickels to go and then bragged on the street corners.

I tried a different approach. "How did you get in this, Mary?"

"Nuts. It's a long story, but I wouldn't tell you."

"Listen. I'm not trying to pry into your life. I want you to talk about this, the whole thing. Something you say may have no meaning to you, but may throw some light on the whole affair. I'm convinced that whatever you are connected with has a contributing factor to Jack's death. I could do it differently. I could slap it out of you. I could wreck this whole setup if I felt like it. But I'm not going to; it would take too long. It's up to you."

"All right. If you think it would help. I wouldn't do it if it weren't for him. In all my life he was one of the very few square guys I ever met. He gave me plenty of breaks, trying to help me, but I failed him, every time. Generally I start bawling when I tell this, but too much water has gone under the bridge to make it upset me anymore."

I sat back and dragged out a cigarette and offered her one. She took it and we lit up. I leaned back on the bed and waited.

"It started in college. I went to the Midwest to become a teacher. It was a co-ed school, and in due time I met a fellow. His name was John Hanson. Tall and good-looking. We intended to get married. One night we parked after a football game and you know what happened. Three months later I had to leave school. John didn't want to get married yet, so he took me to a doctor. When the operation was over I was shaky and nervous. We set up an apartment, John and I, and for a while lived as man and wife without benefit of clergy.

"How my folks got wind of it, I don't know. Those things happen. I got a letter from my father completely disowning me. That same night John didn't come home. I waited and waited, then called the school. He had dropped from the curriculum. Disappeared. My month was nearly up in the apartment and I didn't know what to do.

"Now the unpleasant part. I started to receive visitors. Male visitors. What they offered was the only way I could make any money. That kept on for a few weeks before the landlord found out and kicked me out of the place. No, I didn't walk the streets. A car came and got me and I was driven to a rooming house.

"It wasn't like this. It was dirty and dingy. The madam was an old hag with a mean temper and liked to throw things at us. The first thing she did was to tell me that she had a record of my activities that she would hand over to the police if I didn't cooperate. What could I do?

"Then one night I had a talk with my roommate. She was a character. Tough as an apple and she knew how to sell herself. I told her all that had happened to me and she laughed like a fiend. The same damn thing had happened to her. But here's the hitch. I described John. He was the guy that put her in the spot, too. She flew off the handle when she heard that. Both of us looked all over for him, but that was the last time I saw him.

"I was part of a big outfit. We were shipped around wherever we were needed. I wound up here quite awhile ago and that's that. Any questions?"

The same old story. I felt sorry for her even if she didn't feel sorry for herself. "How long ago were you in college?" I asked.

"That was twelve years ago."

"Umm." As far as I could see there wasn't a thing to be gained. I reached in my wallet and pulled out a five spot and a card. "Here's where you can locate me if you dig up anything else. And here's a fin for yourself. I have some heavy thinking to do so I'm going to blow."

She looked at me amazed. "You mean . . . you don't want anything else?"

"No. But thanks anyway. Keep your eyes open."

"I will."

I found a different way out and hit the downstairs hall from a rickety flight of steps that was half hidden behind a flowered set of drapes. The woman in charge was sitting in the waiting room reading. She put down the book long enough to say, "Leaving already? I thought you wanted to spend the night."

As I picked up my hat, I said, "I did, but I guess I'm not as young as I used to be." She didn't bother to get up to let me out.

Back in the car I started up and ran it closer to the house. I wanted to see who might be coming. Jack had a good reason for wanting that place raided or he wouldn't have mentioned it in his book. A show. A show with convenient chambers for the indiscreet later on. A place that quack doctors like to see well packed so they could work their own racket on suckers that got caught up with V. D. Inwardly, I said a silent thanks to Uncle Sam for showing me those posters and films.

I sat back against the cushions and waited for something to happen. Just what, I couldn't say. So far there was no rhyme or reason to anything. It was too jumpy. Jack's death. The people he was connected with. His book of notes and this. The only thing there was in common was an undertone. The deep tone that spelled hate and violence, a current of fear that seemed to fit in whenever I looked. I could feel it, yet see nothing.

Take Eileen: A prostitute. Taking a quick trip to the grave because she got messed up with a rat who knocked her up, played with her awhile, then took off. That kind of guy ought to be hunted down and strung up by the thumbs. I'd like to do it personally. And her roommate. Another dame in the same profession who got there the same way. It must have made Eileen feel pretty low when she found out the same guy put her in the fix, too. John Hanson, never heard of him. She might have been a decent kid, too. Those guys get it in the neck in the long run. But that was over twelve years ago. That would make Eileen about . . . let's see, entered college around eighteen . . . maybe she met him when she was nineteen, and twelve would put her at thirty-one. Hell, she looked a lot older. If her father had been the least bit sensible he could have prevented all this. A kind word when kindness was important, a home to go to, and she never would have been trapped. Just the same, it seemed pretty damned funny that the old man could get wind of what went on in a Midwest college when he was living a thousand miles away in Poughkeepsie, New York. That kind of news travels fast anywhere, though. Probably a jealous schoolgirl with a dirty mind and a poison pen. Maybe another of Hanson's babes. I'll bet he had plenty of them. Going from bad to worse. Not financially— Eileen was making plenty of cash even if she only got a ten-percent cut. The joint she worked in had money written all over it. A syndicated outfit with lots of the long green. For instance, this show tonight. It meant a rake-off in the thousands. And . . .

I was letting my mind ramble on so fast I hardly noticed the taxi that pulled up in front of the stoop. A young punk in a double-breasted suit stepped out and gave a hand to the fat boy with him. A greasy slob, coming in for the show or some fun, maybe both. I thought I recognized the kid from a bookie's uptown, but I wasn't sure. The fat guy I had never seen before. There were no questions at the door, so I supposed they were well known there.

Five minutes later another car drove up and a pair of dillies climbed out. The man, if you could call him that, was done up in a camel's-hair coat, his skinny neck protruding above a flaming-red ascot. He had a marcel that was brand-new. His companion was a woman. The only way you could tell was by the skirt. The rest of her was strictly male. She walked with a swagger and he minced his way to the sidewalk holding on to her arm. Fruit.

She did the bell ringing and pushed him in ahead of her. Fine people. There's everything in this world. It's too bad they were hiding behind the door when sexes were handed out. They got what was left over and not enough of it at that.

I sat there a whole hour watching a cross section of humanity that came from every walk of life. If I had an infrared camera I could have made a fortune. Eileen probably wasn't well read enough to identify persons as being important, but I was. There were four politicians from my own ward there. Plus a few who hardly skipped a week without having their pictures in the papers for something or other. Everyone was going in, no one coming out. That meant the show was on. Generally a half hour was enough time to transact their kind of business.

Twenty minutes went by and no more cars. If Jack had expected to snag somebody in there it wasn't anyone at the party or someone whom he had connections with that I knew about. I didn't get it.

Then I did. Or at least I thought I did.

I started the motor and pulled away from the curb, then made a U turn in the middle of the block. I tried to beat out the red lights, but the traffic got away from me. Even the shortcuts didn't help, so I cut back to the main thoroughfare and took it straight up to Jack's apartment.

This time I went in the front door. I broke the seal and the flimsy padlock with my gun butt and opened the lock with one of my skeleton keys. Before I did anything else I went for the phone hoping that it hadn't been disconnected. It hadn't. I dialed my number and waited. Then, "Police Headquarters."

"Hello, give me Captain Chambers, Homicide. Shake it." Pat was on in an instant.

"Captain Chambers speaking."

"Pat, this is Mike Hammer, I'm at Jack's apartment. Listen, get a couple of men and whip up here, and if you took any books from here bring them along. One other thing. Better tell the riot squad to stand by for an emergency call."

Pat grew excited. "What's up, Mike, got anything?"

"I may have," I answered, "but if you don't snap it up I may lose it." I hung up before he could ask any more questions. I turned on the lamp in the living room and pulled out what books were lying between cast bronze ends and stacked in the bookcase. I found what I was looking for. Three of them were college yearbooks, and they were dated from the past fifteen years. I remembered having seen them when I was in the apartment the last time. They didn't mean much then, but they did now.

While I was waiting for Pat I scanned through them. They were student publications, all from Midwestern schools. What I was looking for was a picture of John Hanson.

It might be that simple. Jack saw Eileen after a long time and knew what she was doing. A cop wouldn't have much trouble checking those things. He knew what happened to her and he knew the guy. On the flyleaf of each book was the name and address of a secondhand bookstore near Times Square, and the tab it was typed on was clean, so they had been recently bought. If Jack had tracked the guy down and approached him he set himself up for murder. Maybe the guy had a business or a family, but what he had could easily be wrecked by having that kind of information passed on to the wrong people.

I went through them fast, then again very carefully, but there was no picture labeled with the name Hanson. I was cursing softly to myself when Pat came in. Under his arm he had three more of the same kind of books.

"Here you are, Mike," he said, dumping the books on the sofa beside me. "Now give." In as few words as possible I told him where I stood. He watched me gravely and made me repeat a few things to keep track of things in his mind.

"So you think this Eileen Vickers may be the key, huh?"

I signified with a nod of my head. "Possibly. You go through these books and look for the guy. She said he was tall and good-looking, but dames in love all think their men are good-looking. By the way, why did you pick up these books?"

"Because these three were in the living room, open. He was reading them just before he was killed. It seemed funny to me that he should be going through old college yearbooks and I took them along to match the pics with some of our samples."

"And . . . ?"

"And I found two women who had been committed for bigamy, one guy that later hung for murder, and a friend of mine who runs a hardware store downtown and I see every day. Nothing else."

The both of us sat down and read those damn books from cover to cover. When we were done we traded and read them again to make sure we didn't skip anything. John Hanson was nowhere to be found.

"Looks like a wild-goose chase, Mike." Pat was frowning at the pile. He stuck a cigarette in his mouth and lit it. "Are you sure that was what Jack was looking for?"

"Hell, yes, why not? The dates on these things tie in. They're twelve years old." I dragged the black book out of my hip pocket and tossed it to him. "Take a look," I said, "and don't tell me I was withholding evidence."

As Pat glanced through it he said, "I won't. I was up here the day after you. Found it under the bottom drawer of his dresser, didn't you?"

"Yeah, how did you know?"

"At home I happened to drop something over the back of a drawer like that myself. When I thought it over, I knew it was one place we hadn't looked. Incidentally, I found your note."

He finished with the pad and stuck it under his coat. I didn't need it anymore. "I think you may be right, Mike. Where to now?"

"The bookstore. Jack may have had other books. I should have asked Eileen what school she went to, damn it, but I didn't catch on until later."

Pat went to the phone book and thumbed through it until he found the number of the bookstore. The place was closed, but the owner was still there. Pat told him who he was and to stay put until we arrived. I turned out the lights and we left after Pat posted one of his men at the door.

I didn't bother with the jalopy. We piled into the squad car and headed for Times Square with the siren wailing. Traffic pulled off to one side to let us pass and we made record time. The driver turned off on Sixth and stopped across the street from the bookstore.

The blinds were drawn, but a light still glowed from within. Pat knocked and the weazened little proprietor fussed with the lock and let us in. He was nervous as a hen with a yardful of chicks and kept pulling at the bottom of his vest. Pat got to the point after he flashed his badge.

"You had a customer come in here a few days ago and buy several college yearbooks." The little guy shook all over. "Do you keep a record of the sales?"

"Yes and no. We record the sales tax, yes, but the books we don't keep. This is old stock as you can see."

"Never mind," Pat said. "Do you remember what ones he took out with him?"

The guy hesitated a second. "N-no. Maybe I can find out, yes?"

With the little guy leading the way, we went to the rear of the store and he climbed a rickety ladder to the top shelf. "We don't have many calls for these. I remember we had about two dozen. Ah, yes. There are perhaps ten gone."

Ten. Three were in Jack's apartment, and Pat had three. That left four unaccounted for. "Hey," I called up to him, "can you remember what schools they were from?"

He shrugged his skinny shoulders. "I don't know. They have been here a long time. I didn't even take them down. I remember I was busy and showed him where they were and he climbed up and got them."

This wasn't getting us anyplace. I shook the ladder and he grabbed the wall for support. "Take 'em all down," I told him. "Just toss them to me. Come on, we haven't got all night."

He pulled the books from the shelves and let them tumble to the floor. I caught a few, but the rest spilled all over. Pat helped me carry them to the wrapping table, then the little guy came over to join us. "Now," I said to him, "get out your invoices. These must have been signed for when you bought 'em and I want to see the receipts."

"But that was so long ago, I—"

"Damn it, shake your tail before I boot it all over the store. Don't be piddling around with me!" He shot off like a scared rabbit.

Pat laid his hand on my arm. "Slack off, Mike. Remember, I work for the city and this guy is a taxpayer."

"So am I, Pat. We just haven't got time to fool around, that's all."

He was back in a minute with an armful of dusty ledgers. "Some place in here I have the items marked. You want to look for them now?" I could see he was hoping we'd take them along, otherwise it would mean an all-night job. Pat knew that, too, but he used his head. He called headquarters and asked for a dozen men. Ten minutes later they were there. He told them what to look for and passed the ledgers out.

The guy was a hell of a bookkeeper. His handwriting was hardly legible. How he arrived at his balances I didn't know, but I wasn't after that. I threw down the ledger I had after a half hour and picked up another. I was in the middle of the second when a patrolman called Pat over.

He pointed to a list of items. "This what you're looking for, sir?"

Pat squinted at it. "Mike. Come here."

There it was, the whole list, bought at one time from an auctioneer who had sold the estate of a deceased Ronald Murphy, a book collector.

"That's it," I said. We took the list to the table and compared it with the books there while Pat was dismissing the men. I found the four that were missing. One was from the Midwest, the others were from schools in the East. Now all we had to do was to get a copy of the yearbooks from somewhere.

I handed the list to Pat. "Now locate them. I haven't got an idea where we'll do it."

"I have," Pat said.

"Where?" I asked hopefully.

"Public library."

"At this time of night?"

He gave me a grin. "Cops do have some privileges," he told me. Once again he got on the telephone and made a few calls. When he was done he called the bookman over and pointed to the mess we had made of his wrapping desk. "Want us to help you with that?"

The guy shook his head vigorously. "No, no. In the morning is plenty of time. Very glad to help the police. Come again if you want." The city was full of self-respecting citizens. He'll probably want a ticket fixed sometime and come knocking on Pat's door— as if that could help him in this town.

Pat's calls were very effective. They were waiting for us when we got to the library. An elderly gentleman, looking extremely nervous, and two male secretaries. We passed through the turn-stile and a guard locked the door behind us.

The place was worse than a morgue. Its high, vaulted ceilings were never reached by the feeble light that struggled to get out of the bulbs. Our footsteps echoed hollowly through the corridors and came back to us in dull booming sounds. The statues seemed to come alive as our shadows crossed them. The place was a bad spot to be in at night if you had the jitters.

Pat had told him what we were looking for and we wasted no time. The elderly librarian sent his two men somewhere into the bowels of the building and they returned in ten minutes with the four yearbooks.

We sat down there under the light of a table lamp in a reading room and took two books apiece. Four books. Jack had had them and somebody had taken them. He had ten altogether, but the others hadn't been of any use to the one that stole the rest.

The librarian peered at us intently over our shoulders. We flipped page after page. I was about to turn the last leaf of the sophomore section over when I stopped. I found John Hanson. I couldn't speak, I just stared. Now I had the whole picture.

Pat reached out and tapped my hand and pointed to a picture. He had found John Hanson, too. I think Pat caught on as quickly as I did. We both reached for another book and went through them, and we both found John Hanson again. I threw the books on the table and yanked Pat to his feet.

"Come on," I said.

He raced after me, stopping long enough in the main lobby to put through another call for a squad. Then we shot past a star-tled guard and dashed to the curb and into the police car. Pat really let the siren go full blast and we threaded our way through traffic. Ahead of us we saw the blinking red light of the police truck and pulled up on it. Another car came out of a side street and joined us.

The same cars were still there. The police blocked the street off at either end and fell in behind Pat and me as we went up the stoop. This time there were no three longs and a short. A fire ax crashed against the lock and the splintered door swung inward.

Somebody screamed and others picked it up. The place was a bedlam, but the cops had it under control in a minute. Pat and I didn't stick around downstairs. He let me lead the way through the modern waiting room, up the stairs and into the room on the landing. It was empty. We took the door off the small foyer into the hall of doors and ran to the next to last one on the left.

The door opened under my touch and a blast of cordite fumes stung my nostrils. Eileen Vickers was dead. Her body was completely nude as she lay there on the bed, eyes staring vacantly at the wall. A bullet hole was directly over the heart, a bullet hole that was made by a .45.

We found John Hanson, all right. He lay at the foot of the bed with his head in a puddle of his own blood and brains, and with a hole squarely between the eyes. On the wall was more of his goo, with the plaster cracked from where the bullet entered.

He was a mess, this John Hanson. At least that's what he called himself. I called him Hal Kines.

chapter 9

WE LEFT the place exactly as it was. Pat whistled for a patrolman and had him stand guard inside the door. All exits to the house had been blocked off, and the crowd milled within the ring of cops on the main floor. Two other captains and an inspector joined us. I threw them a nod and ran for the back of the house.

Those shootings had taken place not two minutes before we came in. If the killer wasn't in the crowd he was just around the corner. I found the back door in a hurry. It led into an undersized yard that was completely surrounded by an eight-foot-high fence. Someone had taken the trouble to keep the grass cut and the place cleaned out. Even the fence had been whitewashed.

I went around that place looking for prints, but the grass hadn't been trampled in a week. If anyone had gone over that fence he certainly would have left some sort of a mark. There was none. The cellar opened into the place, but the door was locked from the outside with a padlock; so was the door that led between the building and the one next door. The killer never took the back way.

I jumped the steps into the small kitchen and went through the hall to the showroom. Quite a place. All the restraining partitions had been torn down and a stage set up at one end. The cops had the audience back in the cushioned movie-type seats and the girls of the show herded into a compact group on the stage.

Pat came at me from across the room. "What about the back?" he asked breathlessly.

"Nothing doing. He didn't go that way."

"Then the killer is in here. I couldn't find a place even a mouse could get out. The streets are blocked and I got some men behind the houses."

"Let's go over the gang here," I said.

The both of us went down the rows of seats looking over the faces that didn't want to be seen. There was going to be a lot of fixing done tomorrow if some of these jokers didn't want to lose their happy homes. We searched every face. We were looking for George Kalecki, but he either got out in time or never was there.

Neither was the madam.

The homicide boys arrived and we went to Eileen's room. They found what I expected them to find. Nothing. Downstairs I could hear the anguished wails of the girls and the louder voices of some of the men yapping in pretty determined tones. How the commissioner was going to get around this was beyond me.

When the pics were taken Pat and I took a good look of what was left of Hal Kines. With a pencil I traced a few very faint lines along his jawline.

"Very neat, isn't it?"

Pat shot a quick look at me. "Neat enough, but tell me about it. I know who, but not why."

I had difficulty keeping my voice under control as I spoke. "Hal isn't a college kid. I caught that when I saw a shot of him and George against the background of the *Morro Castle*, but I never fitted it in. This bastard was a procurer. I told you George had his finger in the rackets. I thought it was the numbers, but it turned out to be more than that. He was part of a syndicate that ran houses of prostitution. Hal did the snatch jobs, oh, very subtly, then turned them over to George. It wouldn't surprise me if Hal had been the big cheese."

Pat looked more closely at the lines on his face and pointed out a few more just under his hairline. They were hard to see because the blood had matted the hair into a soggy mass.

"Don't you see, Pat," I went on. "Hal was one of these guys who looked eternally young. He helped nature a bit with a few plastic-surgery operations. Look at those yearbooks we found, every one from a different college. That's where he got his women, small-town girls going to an out-of-state school. Knocks them up, puts the squeeze on them and here they are. God knows how many he got from each place. I bet he never spent more than one semester in a place. Probably worked out a scheme for falsifying his high-school records to gain admittance, then got busy with his dirty work. Once he had the dames, they couldn't get out of it any more than a mobster can break away from the gang."

"Very cute," Pat said, "very cute."

"Not too," I told him. "This wrecks my theory. I had him slated for the first kill, but I know now he didn't do it. Jack got on to him somehow, and either Hal saw the books in his apartment and caught wise or the other one did. This was why Jack wanted the place raided tonight, before this could happen. He knew Hal would be here and he wanted him caught with his pants down. If I had taken his advice Eileen might have been alive."

Pat walked over to the wall and dug the slug out of the plaster with a penknife. The one in Eileen hadn't gone all the way through; the coroner was busy dislodging it. When he had it out he handed it to Pat. Under the light Pat examined them carefully before he spoke. Then, "They're both .45s, Mike. And dumdums."

He didn't have to tell me that. "Somebody sure likes to make sure they stay dead," I said through tight lips. "The killer again. There's only one. The same lousy bastard that shot Jack. Those slugs will match up sure as hell. Damn," I spat out, "he's kill crazy! Dumdums in the gut, head and heart. Pat, I'm going to enjoy putting a bullet in that crazy son of a bitch more than I enjoy eating. I'd sooner work him over with a knife first."

"You're not going to anything of the sort," Pat remarked softly.

The coroner's men got the bodies out of there in a hurry. We went downstairs again and checked with the cops who were taking down the names and addresses of the people. The patrol wagon was outside and the girls were loading into it. An officer came up to Pat and saluted him.

"No one got through the line, sir."

"Okay. Have some men hold and the rest search the alleyways

and adjacent buildings. Make everyone identify himself satisfactorily or arrest them. I don't care who they are, understand?"

"Yes, sir." The cop saluted and hurried away.

Pat turned to me. "This madam, would you recognize her again?"

"Hell, yes. Why?"

"I have a folder of persons convicted or suspected of running call houses at the office. I want you to look them over. We got her name from the girls, or at least the only name they knew her by. She was called Miss June. None of the guests here knew her at all. Half the time one of the girls answered the door. She always came herself if the proper signal wasn't given."

I held Pat back a moment. "But what about George Kalecki. He's the guy I want."

Pat grinned. "I have the dragnet out for him. Right now a thousand men are looking for the guy. Think you stand a better chance?"

I let that one ride. Before I went looking for George Kalecki I wanted to do a few other things first. Even if he was the killer, there were others behind the racket that had to be nailed and I wanted them all, not just the trigger puller. It was like a turkey dinner. The whole outfit would be the meal, the killer the dessert. I wish I knew how Jack had gotten the lead on Hal. Now I would never know.

But Jack had connections. Maybe he had run across Hal before, or knew Kalecki's end of it and suspected the rest, and when he met up with Eileen, put two and two together. A guy that operated as long as Hal had couldn't cover himself completely. There had to be a break in the trail somewhere. Whatever Jack did, he did it fast. He knew right where to look to find John Hanson, and he found him the way we did and maybe plenty more times—in the yearbooks of the colleges.

Even if Hal killed Jack, how did his own murderer get the gun? That weapon was as hot as the killer and not a toy to be passed around. No, I didn't think Hal killed Jack. He might have spotted the books and told someone else. That would be the killer. That was what the killer was after. Or was it? Maybe it was just incidental. Maybe the killer only had a remote tie-up with Hal. If that was it Jack was killed for another reason, and the killer, knowing there still was the bare possibility of being traced through that tie-up, didn't take the chance and swiped the books to keep Hal clean.

And where the hell did that leave me? Right up the creek again. I couldn't sit back and wait for something to happen again and work from there. Right now I had to start thinking. Little things were beginning to show their heads. Not much, but enough to show that behind it all was a motive. I didn't see it yet, but I would. I wasn't after a killer now. I was after a motive.

I told Pat that I was going home to bed and he wrote me a pass to get through the police lines. I walked down the street and gave the note to a red-faced cop and went on. A cruising cab came by and I grabbed it to Jack's apartment. My buggy was still outside, and after I paid off the cabby I got in my own heap. There was a lot of work to do tomorrow and I needed some sleep.

Twenty minutes later I was home in bed smoking a cigarette before I went to sleep, still thinking. I couldn't get anywhere, so I crushed out the butt and turned over.

My first stop after breakfast was Kalecki's apartment. As I expected, Pat had been there before me. I asked the cop on duty at the entrance if there was any message for me and he handed over a sealed envelope. I ripped the flap open and pulled out a sheet of paper. Pat had scrawled. "Mike . . . nothing here. He pulled out without bothering to pack a bag." He signed it with a large "P." I tore the note up and dumped the pieces in a trash basket outside the apartment house.

It was a fine day. The sun was warm and the streets full of kids making a racket like a pack of squirrels. I drove to the corner and stopped in a cigar store where I put in a call to Charlotte's office. She wasn't there, but her secretary had been told to tell me that if I called, I could find her in Central Park on the Fifth Avenue side near 68th Street.

I drove in from the cutoff on Central Park West and drove all around the place, circling toward Fifth. When I came out I parked on 67th and walked back to the park. She wasn't on any of the benches, so I hopped the fence and cut across the grass to the inside walk. The day had brought out a million strollers, it seemed like. Private nurses in tricky rigs went by with a toddler at their heels, and more than once I got the eye.

A peanut vendor had just finished giving me change when I saw Charlotte. She was pushing a baby carriage toward me, waving her hand frantically to catch my attention. I hurried up to her.

"Hello, kitten," I said. It made my mouth water to look at her. This time she had on a tight green suit. Her hair resembled a waterfall cascading over her collar. Her smile was brighter than the day.

"Hello, Mike. I've been waiting for you." She held out her hand and I took it. A firm grip, not at all like a woman's. Without letting go I hooked her hand under my arm and fell behind the carriage. "We must look like the happiest newlyweds in the world," she laughed.

"Not so new," I said, motioning toward the carriage. Her face flushed a little and she rubbed her head against mine. "How come you're not working?" I asked her.

"On a day like this? Besides, I don't have an appointment until two, and a friend asked me if I would mind her child while she attended to some business."

"Like kids?"

"I love them. Someday I'm going to have six of my own."

I whistled. "Wait up, take it easy. Maybe I won't make that much money. Six mouths are a lot to feed."

"So what, I'm a working girl, and, er, is that a proposal, Mr. Hammer?"

"Could be," I grinned. "I haven't been pinned down yet, but when I look at you I'm ready to be."

If the conversation had gone any further there's no telling where it would have wound up. But I got back to the case again. "By the way, Charlotte, have you seen the morning papers?"

"No, why?" She glanced at me curiously.

"Hal Kines is dead."

Her jaw dropped and wrinkles of amazement appeared in her forehead. "No," she breathed heavily. I took a tabloid out of my back pocket and showed her the headlines. I could see that she was taken aback. "Oh, Mike, that is terrible! What happened?"

I pointed toward an empty bench. "Can we sit down a few minutes?"

Charlotte consulted her watch and shook her head. "No," she

told me, "I have to meet Betty in a few minutes. Tell you what, walk me to the gate, then we can drive back to my office for a few drinks after I meet her. You can tell me on the way."

I went through the entire previous evening without omitting a detail. Charlotte listened carefully without once asking a question. Her mind was trying for the psychological aspect of it. I had to stop near the end. Betty was waiting for her. After the introduction, we had a few minutes' chat and said good-bye to Betty, who walked off with the baby.

We went in the other direction, following the stone wall of the fence to 67th. I don't think we had gone more than ten feet, when a car pulled abreast of us. No time to think. I saw the ugly snout of the gun sticking out the window and landed in a heap on Charlotte. The bullet smashed against the wall waist high, throwing rock splinters in our faces. George Kalecki didn't have time for a second shot. He threw the car into gear and went tearing down Fifth Avenue. If it had worked it would have been perfect. No other cars around to give chase. For the first time, not even a taxi.

I picked Charlotte up and dusted her off. Her face was white and shaken, but her voice was steady enough. Two strollers came hurrying up, thinking we had fallen. Before they reached us, I got the slug from the dirt under the wall where it had dropped. It was a .45. I thanked the two who tried to help us, explaining that we had tripped, and we went on.

Charlotte waited a moment, then said: "You're getting close, Mike. Somebody wants you out of the way."

"I know it. And I know who that was—our friend, Kalecki." I gave a short laugh. "He's scared. It won't be long now. That skunk is ready to break any minute. If he weren't he wouldn't make a play for me in broad daylight."

"But, Mike, please don't laugh about it. It wasn't that funny."

I stopped and put my arms around her shoulders. I could feel her trembling a little. "I'm sorry, darling. I'm used to being shot at. You might have gotten hit, too. Let me take you home, you'll have to change your clothes. That spill didn't do you much good."

Charlotte didn't speak much riding home. She started to, but stopped. Finally I said, "What is it, Charlotte?"

She frowned a little. "Do you think it was because of the rash promise you made to Jack after he was killed that Kalecki wants you out of the way?"

"Maybe. That's the best reason I know of. Why?"

"Could it be that you know more than anyone else concerning this whole affair?"

I thought that over a moment before I said, "I don't think so. The police have every bit of information I have except, perhaps, the incentive and the personal insight I picked up."

We drove on in silence after that. It was nearly ten o'clock when we got to the apartment. We went up the stairs instead of waiting for the elevator and rang the bell. No one came to the door and Charlotte fumbled for her key. "Damn," she said. "I forgot this is the maid's day off." We went inside and the bell rang again when we opened the door.

"Make a drink while I shower, Mike." Charlotte laid a bottle of bourbon on the coffee table and went into the kitchen for some ice and ginger ale.

"Okay. Do you mind if I use your phone first?"

"Not at all. Go right ahead," she called back.

I dialed Pat's number and had to wait for the operator to go through a half-dozen extensions before he finally located him. "Pat?"

"Yeah, Mike, go ahead."

"Get this. Kalecki didn't take a powder, he's still in the city."

"How do you know?"

"He tried to dust me off a little while ago."

Pat listened intently as I gave him the details. When I got through, he asked: "Did you get the number of the car?"

"Uh-uh. It was a late-model Caddy, about a '41. Dark blue with lots of chrome. He passed me going toward the city."

"Swell, Mike, I'll put it on the air. Have you got the bullet with you?"

"Hell, yes. And it's a .45, too. Better get ballistics to check it. This one wasn't a dumdum, though. Just a nice normal slug. Suppose I drive down to see you this afternoon."

"Do that," Pat answered. "I'll be here the rest of the day unless something breaks.

"And one other thing, Mike," he added.

"Yeah?"

"We checked the slugs that killed Kines and the Vickers woman."

"They came from the same gun? The one that . . ."

"Right, Mike. The killer again."

"Damn," I said.

I hung up and took the slug from my pocket. Maybe it would match, maybe not. I was thinking of the rod Kalecki had in his luggage under his bed. And he had a permit for it too, he said. I wished now that I had taken that gun along to compare it in a ballistics box instead of leaving it to my sense of smell and sight to determine whether or not it had been fired recently.

I wrapped the hunk of metal in a wad of paper and stuck it in my pocket, then whipped up a pair of highballs. I called out to Charlotte to come and get it, but she yelled for me to bring it in to her.

Maybe I should have waited a second, or knocked. I did neither. Charlotte was standing beside the bed completely naked. When I saw her beautiful body that way my blood boiled inside me and the drink shook in my hand. She was more beautiful than I imagined. So damned smooth. She was more startled than I. She made a grab for the robe on the bed and held it in front of her, but not before I saw a blush suffuse her entire body.

She was having as hard a time getting her breath as I was. "Mike," she said. Her voice trembled slightly when she spoke, and her eyes never left mine. I turned my back while she slipped into the robe, then turned back and handed her the drink.

Both of us finished them in one draught. It added nothing to the fire that was running through me. I felt like reaching out and squeezing her to pieces. We put the glasses down on the dresser top. We were awfully close then. One of those moments.

She came into my arms with a rush, burying her face in my neck. I tilted her head back and kissed her eyes. Her mouth opened for me and I kissed her, hard. I knew I was hurting her, but she didn't pull away. She returned that kiss with her lips, her arms and her body. She was on fire too, trying desperately to get close to me through space that wasn't there anymore.

I had my arm around her shoulders and my hands fastened in her hair, crushing her to me. Never before had I felt like this, but then, never before had I been in love. She took her mouth away from mine and lay in my arms, limp, breathing heavily, her eyes closed.

"Mike," she whispered, "I want you."

"No," I said.

"Yes. You must."

"No."

"But, Mike, why? Why?"

"No, darling, it's too beautiful to spoil. Not now. Our time will come, but it must be right."

I put my arm under her and carried her out of the room. If I stayed in that bedroom any longer I couldn't have held on to my sanity. I kissed her again as she lay in my arms, then put her down outside the bathroom door and mussed her hair. "Go take your shower," I said in her ear.

She smiled at me through sleepy eyes and entered, then closed the door softly. I picked up the glasses, and for a brief second eyed the bed, longingly. Maybe I was a damned fool, I don't know. I went on into the living room.

I waited until I heard the shower running before I picked up the phone. Charlotte's secretary answered promptly with the usual hello.

"This is Mike Hammer again," I said. "I'm expecting a friend and I told him to call your office, so when he does, tell him where I went, will you?"

"Oh, that won't be necessary," she replied. "He already has. I told him you'd be in the park. Did you miss him?"

"No, he'll be along," I lied.

So, somebody is on my tail, I told myself as I hung up. Good old George. Followed me, lost me, but figured I'd see Charlotte, very clever.

I made another drink, then stretched out on the sofa. He must have tailed me and I never got wise. I couldn't figure how he knew I'd see Charlotte unless it was written all over me. They say love is like that. But what a way to get put on the spot. He picked the time and place nicely. If I hadn't ducked, Kalecki would have scored a bull's-eye. He did his shooting at point-blank range. What the hell, Kalecki knew the score. If the cops picked him up in the dragnet it would be a miracle. I'll bet he had plenty of places he could hole up in if the time came. George was a smart apple. I wasn't worried about the police flushing him anymore. Mr. Kalecki was reserved—for me. Pat was going to be awfully sore.

Charlotte was out and dressed in record time. Neither of us spoke about what had happened, but each knew that it was foremost in the other's mind. She made herself a drink, then sat down beside me. "How did you know I was coming today?"

She gave me a bright smile. "Mike, darling, I've been expecting you ever since I saw you. Or am I doing it wrong?"

"Not as far as I'm concerned."

"But you told me that you like to do the chasing."

"Not with you. Time is too damned important."

When she settled in my arms I told her about the call to her office. She didn't like it a bit. "You're not trying to be very careful, Mike. If it is Kalecki, he is smart. Please, Mike, watch yourself. If anything happens to you, I'll . . ."

"You'll what?"

"Oh, Mike, can't you see that I love you?"

I stroked her golden hair and blew in her ear. "Yes, silly, I can see it. It must be sticking out all over me the same way."

"Yes," she said, "it is." We both grinned at each other. I felt like a school kid. "Now, let's get back to business before I rush off to the office," she went on. "You came to see me for something besides just being nice. What was it?"

It was my turn to be amazed. "Now, how the hell did you know that?" I demanded.

Charlotte patted my hand. "How many times do I have to remind you that I am a practicing psychiatrist? It doesn't mean that I can read minds, but I can study people, observe their behavior and determine what lies underneath. Especially," here she gave a coy smile, "when you really take an interest in a person."

"You win." I blew a couple of smoke rings and continued. "What I want is everything you know about Hal Kines."

She came back to earth abruptly at the mention of his name. "That's what I thought after you spoke about what happened. Well, you know that he was in a medical school. Pre-med to be exact. From what you said, he was there ostensibly to procure women for this vice syndicate. Isn't that an unusual way of doing it?"

"No. Not when you know people," I said. "In order to have a good hold on the girls they have to break them away from their homes, then get them trapped in the mill. I imagine they have some sort of evidence concerning their activities that they hold over their heads. So what can the girls do? They've been betrayed, kicked out of their homes, no one to turn to, but the door is open to the old profession. At least they can eat and have a roof over their heads—and make plenty of cash. Then once they're in they can't get out even if they wanted to. It takes time, but it's big business and pays off. Using a method like this, Hal could get the girl he wanted without running too much of a personal risk."

"I see." She mulled over what I had said a moment, then gave me the rest. "Anyway, I gave a lecture at the school by invitation of the board and, after examining the records and work of the student body specializing in psychiatry, chose several students to study my clinical methods. Hal Kines was one of them. He was an excellent worker, knew what he was doing every minute. He was far in advance of the others.

"At first I credited it to natural ability and a medical home background, but now I can see that it was simply the result of so much training in the field. After sixteen years of being exposed to teaching you are bound to pick up something."

"I guess so," I cut in. "How about his outside contacts?"

"He lived at an apartment hotel three blocks from me while he was here. During the time he was at school he lived in a dorm, I suppose. On weekends he would visit the clinic and stay with Mr. Kalecki. Hal never spoke much about outside matters, he was so wrapped up in his work. He was in a scrape one day and Jack Williams helped him out."

I nodded. "Yeah, I know all about that from Hal himself. What about his personal side? Did he ever make a pass at you?"

"No. Never attempted one. Do you think he might have been, er, after me to join his syndicate?"

"Why, that dirty . . ." I stopped there when I saw her laughing silently at me. "I doubt that. You were too smart to get caught in that kind of web. I think he was with you either to have an excuse to stay in the city, or really study psychiatry to help him in his work."

"Did it ever occur to you that he might have been here to kill Jack?"

That idea wasn't a new one to me. I'd been playing with it all day. "Could have been. I thought it over. Maybe he was here because Jack had already caught on and was making him stay. Jack was soft-hearted, but not when it came to a thing like that. Not being in the department any longer, he couldn't put the screws on him officially, but held something over his head to make him stay."

"Then who killed Jack—Hal?"

"That," I said, "is something I'd give both legs and one arm to know. Just so long as I had one arm to shoot with. And that's something I'm going to find out before long."

"And what about Hal and this girl, Eileen?"

"The killer got them both. The way I see it, Hal Kines went there to kill the girl, but before he got the chance the killer knocked them both off."

"But if that was the case, how would Jack have known he would be there to kill her?"

"You've got something there, Charlotte. Maybe Jack knew he'd be there for some reason. Think so?"

"Perhaps. Either that or he knew the killer would be there, too. But until then the killer hadn't killed, so he had another purpose in the visit. Sounds sort of scrambled, doesn't it?"

"You're not kidding," I laughed. "But as the plot thickens it thins out, too. Whatever the motive, it takes in a lot of people. Three of them are dead, one is running around the city taking potshots at me, and the killer is someplace sitting back quietly giving all of us the horse laugh. What the hell, let him laugh. He won't be doing it much longer. There's too many people working on this case and they'll uncover something. Murder is a hard thing to hide. Pat is setting a fast pace in this race. He wants the trigger-happy son as badly as I do, but I'll be damned if he's going to get him. From now on I'm going to get out in front of Pat and stay there. Let him stick close to my heels; when the time comes for me to put a bullet in the killer's gut I'm going to be alone. Just me, the rat and a single bullet. It'll go in neat, right in the soft part of the belly. One steel-jacketed slug that will be as effective as ten dumdums."

Charlotte was listening intently, her eyes wide. She was making a typical study of me as though she were hearing the story of a confessed murderer and trying to analyze the workings of the mind. I cut it short and gave her a friendly push. "Now you think I'm off my nut, I bet."

"No, Mike, not at all. Have you been like that just since the war? So hard, I mean."

"I've always been like that," I said, "as long as I could remember. I hate rats that kill for the fun of it. The war only taught me a few tricks I hadn't learned before. Maybe that's why I lived through it."

I checked my watch; it was getting late. "If you want to keep your appointment, you'd better hurry."

Charlotte nodded. "Drive me back to the office?"

"Sure. Get your coat."

We drove back slowly, timing it so that we'd have as much time together as possible. We made small talk, mentioning neither the case nor the near affair in the apartment. When we reached Park Avenue, and turned off to stop, Charlotte said, "When will I see you again, Mike?"

"Soon," I answered. "If the joker that called today to see where I went tries it again, have your secretary tell him that I'm meeting you on this corner. Then try to get hold of me and maybe we can ambush the lug. It was Kalecki, all right; your secretary will probably recognize his voice when she hears it again."

"Okay, Mike. What if Mr. Chambers calls on me?"

"In that case, verify the story of the shooting, but forget about the phone call. If we can trap him, I want it to be my own party."

She leaned in and kissed me again before she left. As she walked away I watched the flashing sleekness of her legs disappear around the corner. She was a wonderful woman. And all mine. I felt like I should let out a loud whoop and do a jig.

A car honked behind me, so I threw the car into gear and pulled away from the curb. I was stopped for a red light two blocks away when I heard my name yelled from across the street. The cars alongside me obscured the person, but I could see a brown-suited figure dancing between them trying to get to my jalopy. I opened the door and he got in. "Hello, Bobo," I said. "What are you doing up this way?"

Bobo was all excited over meeting me. "Golly, Mike. Sure is nice seeing you. I work up here. No place special, just all the places." Words bubbled out of him like out of a water faucet. "Where you going?"

"Well, I was going downtown, but maybe I can drive you someplace. Where are you going?"

Bobo scratched his head. "Lessee. Guess I can go downtown first. Gotta deliver a letter around Canal Street."

"Swell, I'll drop you off there."

The light turned and I swung on to Broadway and turned left.

Bobo would wave at the girls on the street, but I knew how he felt. "Hear anything more about Kalecki?" I asked.

He shook his head. "Naw. Something's happened to him. I saw one of the guys today and he ain't working for him no more."

"How about Big Sam's place? No news from there?"

"Nope. Anyway, since you beat up the two jigs nobody will talk to me. They're scared I might get you after 'em." Bobo let out a gleeful chuckle. "They think I'm a tough guy, too. My landlady heard about it and told me to stay away from you. Isn't that funny, Mike?"

I had about as many friends as a porcupine up that way. "Yeah," I said. "How's the bee situation?"

"Oh, good, good, good. Got me a queen bee. Hey. That wasn't true what you said. A queen bee don't need a king bee. It said so in the book."

"Then how are you going to get more bees?" That puzzled him.

"Guess they lay eggs, or something," he muttered.

Canal Street lay straight ahead, so I let Bobo out when I stopped for the red light. He gave me a breezy "so long" and took off down the street at a half trot. He was a good kid. Another harmless character. Nice, though.

chapter 10

PAT was waiting for me on the firing range. A uniformed patrolman took me to the basement and pointed him out. Pat was cursing over a bad score when I tapped him on the shoulder.

"Having trouble, bub?" I grinned at him.

"Nuts. I think I need a new barrel in this gun." He took another shot at the moving target, a figure of a man, and got it high
up on the shoulder.

"What's the matter with that, Pat?"

"Hell, that would just knock him over." Pat was a perfection-
ist. He caught me laughing at him and handed me the gun.
"Here, you try it."

"Not with that." I pulled the .45 out and kicked the slide back. The target popped up and moved across the range. The gun bucked in my hand. I let three go one after the other. Pat stopped the target and looked at the three holes in the figure's head.

"Not bad." I felt like pasting him.

"Why don't you tell me I'm an expert?" I said. "That's shooting where it counts."

"Phooey. You've just been working at it." I shoved the rod under my coat and Pat pocketed his. He pointed toward the elevator.

"Let's go up. I want to check that slug. Got it with you?" I took the .45 out and unwrapped it, then handed it over. Pat studied it in the elevator, but markings weren't defined clearly enough to be certain of anything. A bullet hitting a stone wall has a lot less shape left than one that has passed through a body.

The ballistics room was empty save for ourselves. Pat mounted the slug inside a complicated slide gadget and I turned the lights out. There was a screen in front of us, and on it was focused an image of two bullets. One was from the killer's gun, the other was the slug Kalecki fired at me. My souvenir still had some lines from the bore of the gun that came out under magnification.

Pat turned the bullet around on its mount, trying to find markings that would match with the other. He thought he did once, but when he transposed the images one on top of the other there was quite a difference. After he had revolved the slug several times he flicked the machine off and turned on the lights. "No good, Mike. It isn't the same gun. If Kalecki did the other shooting, he used another gun."

"That isn't likely. If he kept it after the first killing he'd hang on to it."

Pat agreed and rang for one of his men. He handed the bullet over to him and told him to photograph it and place it in the files. We sat down together and I gave him the full details of the shooting and my views on the Kines kill. He didn't say much. Pat is one of those cops who keep facts in their heads. He stores them away without forgetting an item, letting them fume until they come to the surface by themselves.

It constantly amazed me that there were men like him on the force. But then, when you get past the uniforms and into the inner workings of the organization you find the real thinkers. They have all the equipment in the world to work with and plenty of inside contacts. The papers rag the cops too much, I thought, but in the pinch they called the game. Not much went on that they didn't know about. There was vice. As much as in any outfit, but there were still men like Pat that no money could buy. I would have been one myself if there weren't so damn many rules and regulations to tie a guy down.

When I finished, Pat stretched and said, "Nothing I can add to it for you. Wish I could. You've been a great help, Mike. Now tell me one thing. You gave me facts, this time give me an opinion. Who do you think did it?"

"That, chum, is the sixty-four-dollar question," I countered. "If I had any definite idea, you'd have a justified homicide on your hands. I'm beginning to think of someone outside of those we know. Hell, man, look at the corpses we have floating around. And Kalecki on the loose with a rod. Maybe he did it. He has reason to. Maybe it's the guy behind him again. It could fit in with this syndicate that runs the houses of prostitution. Or the numbers racket George worked. Jack could have found out about that, too. Maybe it was a revenge kill. Hal fouled up enough women in his life. Suppose one of them found out how he did it and made a play for him. When she saw that Jack was going to arrest him she killed Jack, then killed Hal, shooting Eileen to keep her from spouting off what she had seen.

"Maybe it wasn't a girl like that. Could be the brother or father of one. Or a boyfriend for that matter. There's lots of angles."

"I thought of that, Mike. For my money, it's the most plausible idea I've had." Pat stood up. "I want you to come upstairs with me. We have a friend of yours there that you might like to see."

A friend? I couldn't begin to guess whom he was talking about. When I queried him about it he smiled and told me to be patient. He led me into a small room. Two detectives were there with a woman. Both of them fired questions at her, but received no answers. She sat with her back to the door and I didn't recognize her until I stood in front of her.

Friend, hell. She was the madam that ran out the night Hal and Eileen were killed.

"Where did you pick her up, Pat?"

"Not far from here. She was wandering on the streets at four a.m. and a patrolman picked her up on suspicion."

I turned to the madam. Her eyes were vacant from the long hours of questioning. She held her arms across her ample breasts in a defiant attitude, though I could see that she was near the breaking point. "Remember me?" I asked her.

She stared at me through sleep-filled eyes a moment, then said dejectedly, "Yes, I remember."

"How did you get out of that house when it was raided?"

"Go to hell."

Pat drew up a chair in front of her and sat backwards on it. He saw what I was driving at right away. "If you refuse to tell us," Pat said quietly, "you're liable to find yourself facing a charge for murder. And we can make it stick."

She dropped her arms at that one and licked her lips. This time she was scared. Then her fear passed and she sneered. "You go to hell, too. I didn't kill them."

"Perhaps not," Pat answered, "but the real killer left the same way you did. How do we know you didn't show him the way? That makes you an accessory and you might just as well have pulled the trigger."

"You're crazy!" Gone was the composure she had the first time I met her. She didn't look respectable any more. By now her hair had a scraggly appearance and the texture of her skin showed through in the light. White, porous skin. She bared her teeth and swallowed. "I—I was alone."

"The charge will still stick."

Her hands fell into her lap and shook noticeably. "No. I was alone. I was at the door when the police came up. I knew what it was. I ran for the exit and left."

"Where is the exit?" I cut in.

"Under the stairs. A button that works the panel is built into the woodwork."

I thought back fast. "All right, so you saw the cops coming. If you ran for the stairs the killer would have been coming down as you ran out. Who was it?"

"I didn't see anybody, I tell you! Oh, why don't you let me alone!" Her nerve broke and she sank into the chair with her face buried in her hands.

"Take her out," Pat directed the two detectives. He looked at me. "What do you make of it?"

"Reasonable enough," I told him. "She saw us coming and beat it. But the killer had a little luck. We broke in about two minutes after the shooting. The rooms are soundproofed and no one heard the shots. The killer probably figured on mixing with the crowd and leaving when the show was over or before, if there was nobody at the door. He was coming down the stairs and heard us.

"However, when the madam made a run for it those plans had to be tossed overboard. He ducked back long enough so the old hag didn't see him and followed her through the secret panel. When we examine it I'll bet we find that it doesn't close very fast. We ran upstairs, you remember, and the others took care of the guests. The way we set the road block, the killer had time to get away before the policemen could take their places. We were in a hurry and didn't have a chance to plan this thing."

I proved to be right. We went back to the house and looked for the panel. It was right where she said it was. The thing wasn't too cleverly contrived. The button was built into the heart of a carved flower. It activated a one sixteenth horsepower motor connected to the electric circuit with a cutoff and a reverse. Pat and I entered the passage. Light seeping through the cracks in the wall was all we needed. When the place was redecorated this was built in. It ran back ten feet, took a sharp left turn and steps led down to the basement. There we were between walls. A door led into the basement of the house next door. When it was closed it looked like a part of the wall.

It was a safe bet that the people in the house didn't know that it was there themselves. The rest was easy. Out the basement

door to an open yard that led to the street. The time consumed
was less than a minute. We went through the passageway with a
searchlight, not skipping an inch, but there wasn't a clue to be
found. Generally when someone was in haste he could be counted
on to lose something or mark a trail. But no such luck. We went
back to the waiting room and pulled out a smoke.

"Well?"

"Well what, Pat?"

"Well, I guess you were right about the timing," he laughed.

"Looks that way. What did you get on Kines' past, if anything?"

"Reports from twenty-seven schools so far. He never spent
more than a semester anywhere except at this last place. More often a month was enough. When he left there were several girls
who'd dropped from the school too. Add it up and you get a nice
tally. We've had a dozen men on the phone all day and they're not
half finished yet."

I thought that over and cursed Hal before I said, "What did he
have in his pockets when the boys went over him?"

"Nothing much. Fifty some in bills, a little loose change, a
driver's license and an owner's certificate for his car. There were
some club cards, too, but of the school. He went around clean.
We found his car. It was empty except for a pair of silk panties in
the glove compartment. By the way, how did he get in here if you
had your eyes open?"

I dragged on the butt, thinking over those that came in here.
"Got me. He never came alone, that's a sure thing. The only way
he could have done it was to impersonate someone by stuffing
pillows or something under his jacket, or . . ." I snapped my fin-

gers. "Now I remember. A crowd of six or more came in and they blocked out a few others that were behind them. They all mingled at the foot of the steps and came in together to get off the street as fast as they could."

"Was he alone?" Pat waited anxiously for my answer.

I had to shake my head. "I can't say, Pat. It does seem funny that he would come in here deliberately with the murderer, knowing that he was going to get knocked off."

The afternoon was running into evening and we decided to call it a day. Pat and I separated outside and I drove home to clean up. The case was beginning to get on my nerves. It was like trying to get through a locked door with a bulldog tearing at you.

So far I had investigated a lot of angles; now I had one more to go. I wanted to find out about that strawberry mark on a certain twin's hip.

I had my dinner sent up from a place down at the corner and polished off a quart of beer with it. It was nearly nine when I put in a call to the Bellemy apartment. A soft voice answered.

"Miss Bellemy?"

"Yes."

"This is Mike Hammer."

"Oh." She hesitated a second, then, "Yes?"

"Is this Mary or Esther?"

"Esther Bellemy. What can I do for you, Mr. Hammer?"

"Can I see you this evening?" I asked. "I have some questions I'd like to ask you."

"Can't they be asked over the phone?"

"Hardly. It would take too long. May I come up?"

"All right. I'll be waiting."

I thanked her and said good-bye, then climbed into my coat and went downstairs to my car.

Esther was the replica of her sister. If there was a difference, I couldn't see it. I hadn't taken time to look for any the first time I met them. Probably all in the personality. Mary was strictly a nymphomaniac; now let's see how this sister was.

She greeted me cordially enough. She was wearing a dinner dress that was a simple thing, cunningly revealing the lovely lines of her body. Like Mary, she too had a tan and the appearance of having led an athletic life. Her hair was different. Esther had hers rolled up into a fashionable upsweep. That was the only thing I objected to. With me, a girl in upswept hair looks like she needs a pail and mop, ready to swab down the kitchen floor. But the way she was otherwise built more than made up for that objection.

I took a seat on the divan I had before. Esther went to a cabinet and took out glasses and a bottle of Scotch. When she came back with the ice and had the drinks poured she said, "What is it you wanted me to tell you, Mr. Hammer?"

"Call me Mike," I said politely. "I'm not used to formalities."

"Very well, Mike." We settled back with the drinks.

"How well did you know Jack?"

"Casually. It was a friendship that comes with constantly meeting after an introduction, but not an intimate one."

"And George Kalecki? How well did you know him?"

"Not well at all. I didn't like him."

"Your sister gave me the same impression. Did he ever make a pass at you?"

"Don't be silly." She thought a moment before continuing.

"He was grouchy about something the night of the party.

Hardly sociable, I'd say. He didn't strike me as being a gentleman. There was something about his manner that was repulsive."

"That isn't unusual. He was a former racketeer. Still active in some circles, too."

When she crossed her legs I couldn't think of anything more to ask her. Why don't women learn to keep their skirts low enough to keep men from thinking the wrong things? Guess that's why they wear them short.

Esther saw my eyes following the outlines of her legs and made the same old instinctive motion of covering up. It didn't do a bit of good. "On with the game," she told me.

"What do you do for a living, if you don't mind?" I knew the answer already, but asked it just to have something to say.

Her eyes glittered impishly. "We have a private income from stock dividends. Father left us his share in some mills down South. Why, are you looking for a rich wife?"

I raised my eyebrows. "No. But if I were I'd be up here more often. What about your home? You have quite an estate, haven't you?"

"About thirty acres in lawn and ten in second-growth woods. A twenty-two-room house sits right in the middle surrounded by a swimming pool, several tennis courts and generally a round dozen ardent swains who never tire of telling me how lovely I am just to get their paws on half of it."

I whistled. "Hell, someone told me you occupied a modest residence." Esther laughed gaily, the sound coming from deep in her throat. With her head tilted back like that she gave me the full view of her breasts. They were as alive as she was.

"Would you like to visit me sometime, Mike?"

I didn't have to think that over. "Sure. When?"

"This Saturday. I'm having quite a few up there to see a tennis match under lights at night. Myrna Devlin is coming. Poor girl, it's the least I can do for her. She's been so broken up since Jack died."

"That's an idea. I'll drive her up. Anybody else coming that I know?"

"Charlotte Manning. No doubt you've met her."

"No doubt," I grinned.

She saw what I meant and wiggled a finger at me. "Don't get any ideas like that, Mike."

I tried to suppress a smile. "How am I going to have any fun in a twenty-two-room house if I don't get ideas?" I teased her.

The laugh in her eyes died out and was replaced by something else. "Why do you think I'm asking you up as *my* guest?" she said.

I put my drink down on the coffee table, then circled it and sat down beside her. "I don't know, why?"

She put her arms around my neck and pulled my mouth down close to hers. "Why don't you find out?"

Her mouth met mine, her arms getting tighter behind me. I leaned on her heavily, letting my body caress hers. She rubbed her face against mine, breathing hotly on my neck. Whenever I touched her she trembled. She worked a hand free and I heard snaps on her dress opening. I kissed her shoulders, the tremble turned into a shudder. Once she bit me, her teeth sinking into my neck. I held her tighter and her breathing turned into a gasp. She was squirming against me, trying to release the passion that was inside her.

My hand found the pull cord on the lamp beside the divan and the place was in darkness. Just the two of us. Little sounds. No words. There wasn't need for any. A groan once or twice. The rustle of the cushions and the rasping sound of fingernails on broadcloth. The rattle of a belt buckle and the thump of a shoe kicked to the floor. Just the breathing, the wetness of a kiss.

Then silence.

After a bit I turned the light back on. I let my eyes rove. "What a little liar you are," I laughed.

She pouted. "Why do you say that?"

"No strawberry mark—Mary."

She gave another chuckle and pulled my hair down in my face. "I thought you'd be interested enough to go looking for it."

"I ought to swat you."

"Where?"

"Forget it. You'd probably like it."

I got up from the divan and poured a drink while Mary readjusted herself. She took the drink from me and polished it off in one gulp. I reached for my hat as I rose to leave. "Does that date still hold for Saturday?" I asked.

"Damn well told," she smirked, "and don't be late."

I sat up late that night with a case of beer. We were coming around the turn into the home stretch now. With a spare pack of butts and the beer handy, I parked in the overstuffed rocker by the open windows and thought the thing out. Three murders so far. The killer still on the loose.

Mentally, I tried to list the things that were still needed to clean up the case. First, what did Jack have that caused his death? Was it the books, or something else? Why did Hal die? Did he go to that house to kill her, to threaten her, to warn her? If the killer was someone I knew how did he follow him in without me seeing him? Plenty to go over here. Lots of probable answers. Which was right?

And George Kalecki. Why was he on the loose? If he had no part in it there was no reason for him to lam. Why did he shoot at me—just because he knew I was after the killer? Possible, and very probable. He had every reason to be the one.

There wasn't a single person at the party who didn't have the opportunity to kill Jack. But motive was another thing. Who had that? Myrna? I'd say no. Purely sentimental reasons.

Charlotte? Hell, no. More sentimental reasons. Besides, her profession didn't go with crime. She was a doctor. Only a casual friend of Jack's through Myrna's sickness. No motive there.

The twins, how about them? One a nymphomaniac, the other I never studied. Plenty of money, no troubles that I knew about. Where did they fit? Did Esther have a motive? Have to find out more about her. And the strawberry mark. Could Mary have been snubbed by Jack? Possible. The way she was, her passions could get the better of her. Could she have made a play for Jack, been rebuffed, then taken it out in murder? If so, why take the books?

Hal Kines. He's dead.

Eileen Vickers. Dead. Too late to do anything about it now.

Could there be two murderers? Could Hal have killed Jack, then killed Eileen, and been in turn killed with his own gun there in the room? A great possibility, except that there was no sign of a struggle. Eileen's nude body. Was she professionally prepared to receive a visitor and surprised when her old lover walked in! Why? Why? Why?

Where was the secret to all this hidden? Who did it? It wasn't in Kalecki's apartment; not in Jack's, unless I couldn't read signs anymore.

Was there an outsider?

Hell. I finished another bottle of beer and set the empty down at my feet. I was slowing up. Couldn't think any more. I wish I knew just where George Kalecki came in. That tie-up would prove important. To me, it looked as if the next step would be to find him. If Hal were alive . . .

I cut my thoughts short and slapped my leg. Damn, how could I be so simple. Hal hadn't operated out of the city. He had been going to school. If he had any record of his operations they were there. And that might be exactly what I needed.

As quickly as I could, I dressed. When I had my coat on I shoved an extra clip of cartridges in my pocket and phoned the garage to bring my car around.

It was almost midnight, and a sleepy attendant drove up as soon as I got downstairs. I stuffed a dollar bill into his hand, hopped in and pulled away. Luckily, there was no traffic to worry about this time of night. I beat out a few lights and turned on the West Side Express Highway and headed north. Pat had told me the town the college was in. Ordinarily it was a good three hours' drive from the city, but I didn't intend to take that long.

Twice the highway patrol came out of a cutoff after me, but they didn't stay with my overpowered load very long. I was a little afraid that they might radio ahead to try to throw up a road block to stop me, but nothing happened.

The signs told me when to turn and I got on an unkept country road that had so many ruts I had to slow down, but when the counties changed, so did the road. It changed into a smooth macadam, and I made the rest of the trip going full out.

Packsdale was five miles ahead. The chamber of commerce sign said it was a town of thirty thousand and the county seat. Huba huba. The college wasn't hard to find. It sat on a hill a mile north of town. Here and there some lights were lit, probably those in the corridors. I slammed on the brakes in time to swing into a gravel drive and roll up to an impressive-looking two-story house squatting a hundred feet back on the campus. The guy must have been in the army. Along the drive he had a yellow and black sign that read: "Mr. Russell Hilbar, Dean of Men."

The house was completely blacked-out, but that didn't stop me. I put my finger on the bell and never took it off until the lights blazed up in the place and I could hear footsteps hurrying to the door. The butler stood there with his mouth open. He had thrown on his working jacket on top of a nightshirt. Most ridiculous sight I ever saw. Instead of waiting to be admitted and announced, I pushed into the room and nearly knocked over a tall, distinguished guy in a maroon dressing robe.

"What is this, sir? Who are you?"

I flashed by badge and he squinted at it. "Mike Hammer, Investigator from New York."

"Aren't you out of your territory?" he stormed. "What do you want?"

"You had a student here named Harold Kines, didn't you? I want to see his room."

"I'm afraid that's impossible. Our county police are handling the affair. I'm sure they are capable. Now if you'll please . . ."

I didn't let him go any further. "Listen, buddy," I pounded on his chest with a stiffened forefinger, "it's quite possible that right now there's a murderer loose on this campus. If he isn't a murderer he's liable to be one if you don't use your knob and tell me where I can find the room. And if you don't," I added, "I'll smack you so hard you'll spill your insides all over the joint!"

Russell Hilbar backed up and grabbed the edge of a chair for support. His face had gone pasty white and he looked ready to faint. "I—I never thought . . ." he stammered, ". . . Mr. Kines' room is on the lower floor in the east wing. The room number is 107, right on the southeast corner. But the county police have closed it pending a further investigation and I have no key."

"The hell with the county police. I'll get in. Turn these lights off and don't move out of the house. And stay away from the phone."

"But the students—will they . . . ?"

"I'll take care of them," I said as I closed the door.

Outside I had to orientate myself to find the east wing. I picked a low rectangular building out to be the dorms and I wasn't wrong. The grass muffled any sounds I made, and I crept up on the corner of the wing. I prayed silently that my hunch wasn't wrong and that I wasn't too late. As much as possible, I stayed in the shadows, working my way behind the bushes set against the wall.

The window was shoulder high, and down all the way. I took off my hat and put my ear close to the pane, but I couldn't detect any sound from inside. I took the chance. My fingers went under the sash and I pushed the window up. It slid without a creak. I jumped, and pulled myself into the room, then slid off the sill and landed on my face.

That fall saved my life. Two shots blasted from the corner of the room. The slugs smashed into the window sill behind me and threw splinters in my face. For a brief moment the room was lit up with the weird red glow of the gunflash.

My hand darted under my coat and came out with my rod. Our shots came almost together. I let three go as fast as my finger could pull the trigger. Something tugged at my jacket and I felt my ribs burn. There was another shot from across the room, but it wasn't directed at me. It went off into the floor of the room and the guy that fired it followed it down.

This time I didn't take a chance. I jumped the gap between us and landed on a body. I kicked for the gun and heard it skid across the floor. Only then did I switch on the lights.

George Kalecki was dead. My three shots had all caught him in the same place, right in the chest around the heart. But he had time to do what he came to do. In one corner, and still warm, was a pile of ashes in a green metal box.

chapter 11

THE next second there was a furious pounding on the door and voices raising cain outside. "Get away from that door and shut up," I yelled.

"Who's in there?" a voice demanded.

"Your uncle Charlie," I shot back. "Now can that chatter and get the dean up here fast as you can and tell him to call the police."

"Watch the window, fellows," the voice hollered. "The door is still sealed and he must have gone in that way. That's it, Duke, take the rifle. No telling who it is."

These crazy college kids. If one of them got jumpy with that rifle I'd be a dead duck. I stuck my head out the window as four of them came tearing around the corner at top speed. When they saw me they stopped in a flurry of dust. I waved to the big tow-headed kid carrying a .22 repeater. "Come here, you."

He marched up to the window with the gun out in front of him like he was going to bayonet somebody. He was scared stiff. I palmed my tin and shoved it under his nose. "See this badge?" I said. "I'm a cop, New York. Now keep your noses out of here. If you want to do something, post a guard around the campus until the cops get here and don't let anyone out. Understand?"

The kid bobbed his head eagerly. He was glad to get away from there. The next second he was shouting orders all over the place. Good ROTC material. The dean came running up blowing like a sick horse. "What happened?" His voice nearly broke when he spoke.

"I just shot a guy. Call the cops and be sure the kids stay out of here." He took off like a herd of turtles and I was left alone save for the curious voices outside the door. What I had to do had to be done before a lot of hayseed county cops took over.

I let George lay where he had fallen, taking time only to notice the gun. It was a .45, same as mine, and the one he had in his room when I searched it. I recognized a scratch on the butt.

The green box was my next step. I sifted the ashes carefully, trying to determine what they had been. The blackened cover of a note pad lay on the bottom, but it dissolved into dust at my touch. These ashes had been one or more books. I would have given a million dollars to know what they had had in them.

Not a word was visible, so thoroughly had George burned them. I looked around the spot on the floor where the box was originally. A few ashes were there, too. One was larger than the rest and not as well burned through. It had a string of numbers on it. I wondered how he concealed the fire. From outside it would have lit the room up as much as the overhead light would have.

I found out in a moment. A throw rug lay on the floor. When I turned it over the underside was blackened. Stuck to the mesh of the weave was a half-page leaf of the paper. It would have gone well at a murder trial. George was named as the trigger man in a murder, and where the proof could be found was also revealed—in a safe-deposit box in an uptown bank. It even gave the number and the code word. The key was in trust with the bank officer.

So George was a murderer. I had always thought he went that far back in the old days. Well, here was something to prove it. At least it more than justified my self-defense act in gunning him down. I tucked the charred bit into a small envelope I carry for things like this, addressed it to myself and put a stamp on it. This time I used the door. I broke the seal with my shoulder and nearly bowled over a half-dozen kids. When I shooed them away I looked around for a post box and found one at the end of the corridor. I dropped it in and went back to wait for the arrival of the cops.

It was coming out now. Heretofore I thought Kalecki was the big wheel behind the syndicate, but now I could see that he was only a small part of it. Hal Kines had been the big shot. His methods were as subtle as those he used in obtaining his women. He went to enough trouble, but it was worth it. First he picked on guys with a dubious past, and ones against whom he wouldn't run into much trouble obtaining evidence. When he compiled it, he presented the stuff, or a photostat, and made the guy work with him. If I could have gotten the information that was burned we could have broken the filthiest racket in the world. Too late now, but at least I had a start. Maybe there were duplicates in the strong box, but I doubted that. Hal probably kept his evidence in different boxes for different people. That way, if he had to put the pressure on the group, he could send a note to the cops to investigate such and such a box without having any of his others disturbed. Nice thinking. Very farsighted.

I felt sort of good over having nailed Kalecki, but he still wasn't the one I wanted. If this kept up there wouldn't be anyone left at all. There was an outsider in this case. There had to be. One that nobody knew about, except, perhaps, those that were dead.

The county police arrived with all the pomp and ceremony of a presidential inaugural address. The chief, a big florid-faced farmer, pranced into the room with his hand on the butt of a revolver and promptly placed me under arrest for murder. Two minutes later, after a demonstration of arm waving, shouting and bulldozing of which I did not think myself capable, he retreated hastily and just as promptly unarrested me. However, to soothe his ruffled feelings I let him inspect my private operator's license, my gun permit and a few other items of identification.

I let him listen to me put in the call to Pat. These county cops have no respect for authority outside their own limits, but when he got on the phone, Pat threatened him with calling the governor unless he cooperated with me. I gave him what details were necessary to keep him busy awhile, then took off for New York.

Going back I took it easier. It was early morning when I stopped outside of Pat's office and my eyes wouldn't stay open. He was waiting for me nevertheless. As quickly as I could I gave him the details of the shooting. He dispatched a car upstate to get photographs and see if there was anything to be learned from the ashes of the burned notebooks.

I didn't feel like going home, so I called Charlotte. She was up and dressed for an early appointment.

"Can you stay put until I get there?" I queried.

"Certainly, Mike. Hurry up. I want to hear what happened."

"Be there in fifteen minutes," I said, then hung up.

It took thirty, traffic was pretty heavy. Charlotte was in the door while Kathy was dusting. She took my coat and hat and I headed for the sofa. I relaxed with a sigh, and she bent down and kissed me. I hardly had enough energy to kiss her back. With her there beside me I told the whole story. Charlotte was a good listener. When I finished she stroked my forehead and my face.

"Is there anything I can do to help?" she asked.

"Yeah. Tell me what makes a nymphomaniac."

"So? You've been to see her again!" Her answer was indignant.

"Business, darling." I wondered when I'd be able to stop using that line.

Charlotte laughed. "That's all right. I understand. As for your question, a nymphomaniac can be either a case of gradual development through environment or born into a person. Some people are oversexed, a glandular difficulty. Others can be repressed in childhood, and when they find themselves in an adult world, no longer the victim of senseless restrictions, they go hog wild. Why?"

I evaded the why and asked, "Can the ones with emotional difficulty go bad?"

"You mean, will they kill as a result of their emotional overload? I'd say offhand, no. They find an easier out for their emotions."

"For instance," I parried.

"Well, if a nymphomaniac showers a great deal of emotion on a person, then is rebuffed, instead of killing the one who spurned her, she simply finds another with whom to become emotionally entangled. It's quicker, besides being more effective. If she suffers a loss of prowess from the rebuff, this new person renews her. See?"

I got what she was driving at, but there was still something else. "Would it be likely for both the twins to be nymphomaniacs?"

Charlotte gave me that delightful laugh. "Possible, but it doesn't happen to be so. You see, I know them rather well. Not too well, but enough to determine their characters. Mary is beyond help. She likes to be the way she is. I daresay she has more fun than her sister, but Esther has seen so many of her escapades and helped her out of trouble, that she has a tendency to turn away from love affairs herself. Esther is a charming enough person, all right. Just about everything her sister has without the craze for men. When a man does drop into Esther's life, she'll take it naturally."

"I'll have to meet her," I said, sleepily. "By the way, are you going up to their place this weekend?"

"Why, yes, Mary invited me. I'll be late getting there, but I won't miss the game. However, I have to come back right after it. Are you going?"

"Uh-huh. I'm going to drive Myrna up. That is, I still have to call her so she'll know about it."

"Swell," she said. That was the last word I heard. I fell into a sleep as deep as the ocean.

When I awoke I glanced at my watch. It was nearly four in the afternoon. Kathy heard me stir and came into the room with a tray of bacon and eggs and coffee.

"Heah's yo' breakfast, Mistah Hammah. Miss Charlotte tell me to take good care of ya'll till she comes home." Kathy gave me a toothy white smile and waddled out after setting the tray down.

I gulped the eggs hungrily and polished off three cups of coffee. Then I called Myrna and she told me that it was okay to pick her up at ten a.m. Saturday. I hung up and poked around the bookshelves for something to read while I waited. Most of the fiction I had read, so I passed on to some of Charlotte's textbooks. One was a honey called *Hypnosis as a Treatment for Mental Disorders.* I skimmed through it. Too wordy. It gave the procedure for putting a patient into a state of relaxation, inducing hypnosis, and suggesting treatment. That way, the patient later went about effecting his own cure automatically.

That would have been a nice stunt for me to learn if I could do it. I pictured myself putting the eye on a beautiful doll and—hell, that was nasty. Besides, I wasn't that bad off. I chose one that had a lot of pictures. This one was titled, *Psychology of Marriage.* Brother, it was a dilly. If it weren't for the big words I would have enjoyed it. I wished they would write stuff like that in language for the layman.

Charlotte came in when I was on the last chapter. She took the book out of my hand and saw what I was reading. "Thinking of anything special?" she asked.

I gave her a silly grin. "Better get the low-down now while I'm able to. Can't say how long I'm going to have the strength to hold off." She kissed me and whipped me up a Scotch and soda. When I downed it I told Kathy to get my hat and coat. Charlotte looked disappointed.

"Have to leave so soon? I thought you'd stay to dinner at least."

"Not tonight, honey. I have a job for my tailor and I want to get cleaned up. I don't suppose *you'd* have a razor handy." I pointed to the bullet hole in my coat. Charlotte got a little white when she saw how close it had come.

"Are . . . are you hurt, Mike?"

"Hell, no. Got a bullet burn across the ribs but it never broke the skin." I pulled up my shirt to confirm it, then got dressed. The phone rang just then and she took it.

She frowned once or twice, said, "Are you sure? All right, I'll look into it." When she hung up I asked her what the matter was. "A client. Responded to treatment, then lapsed into his former state. I think I'll prescribe a sedative and see him in the morning." She went to her desk.

"I'll run along then. Maybe I'll see you later. Right now I want to get a haircut before I do anything else."

"Okay, darling." She came over and put her arms around me. "There's a place on the corner."

"That'll do as well as any," I told her between kisses.

"Hurry back, Mike."

"You bet, darling."

Luckily, the place was empty. A guy was just getting out of the chair when I went in. I hung my coat on a hook and plunked into the seat. "Trim," I told the barber. After he ogled my rod a bit, he draped me with the sheet and the clippers buzzed. Fifteen minutes later he dusted me off and I walked out of there slicked down like an uptown sharpie. I got the boiler rolling and turned across town to get on Broadway.

I heard the sirens wailing, but I didn't know it was Pat until the squad car shot past me and I saw him leaning out of the side window. He was too busy to notice me, but cut across the intersection while the cop on the corner held traffic back. Further down the avenue another siren was blasting a path northward.

It was more a hunch than anything else, the same kind of a hunch that put me on the trail of George Kalecki. And this one paid off, too, but in a way I didn't recognize at first. As soon as the cop on the corner waved us on, I followed the howl of police cars and turned left on Lexington Avenue. Up ahead I saw the white top of Pat's car weaving in and out of the lanes. It slowed down momentarily and turned into a side street.

This time I had to park a block away. Two police cars had the street barred to traffic at either end. I flashed my badge and my card to the patrolman on the corner. He let me pass and I hurried down to the little knot of people gathered outside a drugstore. Pat was there with what looked like the whole homicide bureau. I pushed my way through the crowd and nodded to Pat. I followed his eyes down to the crumpled figure on the sidewalk. Blood had spilled out of the single hole in the back, staining the shabby coat a deep maroon. Pat told me to go ahead and I turned the face around to see who it was.

I whistled. Bobo Hopper would keep bees no longer.

Pat indicated the body. "Know him?"

I nodded. "Yeah. Know him well. His name is Hopper, Bobo Hopper. A hell of a nice guy even if he was a moron. Never hurt anything in his life. He used to be one of Kalecki's runners."

"He was shot with a .45, Mike."

"What!" I exploded.

"There's something else now. Dope. Come over here." Pat took me inside the drugstore. The fat little clerk was facing a battery of detectives led by a heavy-set guy in a blue serge suit. I knew him all too well. He never liked me much since I blew a case wide open under his very nose. He was Inspector Daly of the narcotics squad.

Daly turned to me. "What are you doing here?" he demanded.

"Same thing you are, I think."

"Well, you can start walking as of now. I don't want any private noses snooping around. Go on, beat it."

"One moment, Inspector." When Pat talked in that tone of voice he could command attention. Daly respected Pat. They were different kinds of cop. Daly had come up the hard way, with more time between promotions, while Pat had achieved his position through the scientific approach to crime. Even though they didn't see eye to eye in their methods, Daly was man enough to give Pat credit where credit was due and listen to him.

"Mike has an unusual interest in this case," he continued. "It was through him we got as far as we have. If you don't mind, I would like him to keep in close touch with this."

Daly glared at me and shrugged his beefy shoulders. "Okay. Let him stay. Only be sure you don't withhold any evidence," he spat at me.

The last time I was involved in a case he was working on I had to play my cards close to my vest, but hanging on to the evidence I had led me to a big-time drug dealer we never would have nailed otherwise. Daly never forgot that.

The head of the narcotics bureau was blasting away at the druggist and I picked up every word. "Once more now. Give me the whole thing and see what else you can remember."

Harried to the breaking point, the druggist wrung his pudgy

hands and looked at the sea of faces glaring at him. Pat must have had the most sympathetic expression, so he spoke to him.

"I was doing nothing. Sweeping out under the counter, maybe. That is all. This man, he walks in and says fill a prescription. Very worried he was. He hands me a broken box that has nothing written on the cover. He says to me he will lose his job and nobody will trust him if I can't do it. He drops the box he was delivering and somebody steps on it and his prescription is all over the sidewalk.

"This powder was coming out of the sides. I take it in the back and taste it yet, then test it. Pretty sure I was that I knew what was in it, and when I test it I was positive. Heroin. This should not be, so like a good citizen I phone the police and tell them what I have. They tell me to keep him here, but how do I know that he is not a gangster and will shoot me?" Here the little guy stopped and shuddered.

"I have a family yet. I take my time, but he tells me to hurry up and puts his hand in a pocket. Maybe he has a gun. What can I do? I fill another box with boric acid, charge him a dollar and he walks out. I leave my counter to go see where he goes, but before I get to the door he falls to the sidewalk. He is shot. All the way dead. I call police again, then you come."

"See anyone running off?" Pat asked.

He shook his head. "Nobody. At this time it is slow. Nobody on the street."

"Did you hear a shot?"

"No. That I could not understand. I was too scared. I see the blood from the hole and I run back inside."

Pat stroked his chin. "How about a car. Did any go by at that time?"

The little guy squinted his eyes and thought back. Once he started to speak, stopped, then reassured, said, "Y-yes. Now that you remind me, I think one goes by just before. Yes. I am sure of it. Very slow it goes and it was turning." He continued hurriedly from here. "Like it was coming from the curb maybe. It goes past, then when I am outside it is gone. I don't even look for it after that, so scared I am."

Daly had one of his men taking the whole thing down in short-hand. Pat and I had heard enough. We went outside to the body and checked the bullet angle. From the position of where it lay, the killer had been going toward Lexington when the shot was fired. The packet of boric acid, now a blood red, lay underneath Bobo's hand. We patted the pockets. Empty. His wallet held eight dollars and a library card. Inside the coat was a booklet on the raising of bees.

"Silencer," Pat said. "I'll give ten to one it's the same gun."

"I wouldn't take that bet," I agreed.

"What do you make of it, Mike?"

"I don't know. If Kalecki were alive it would involve him even deeper. First prostitution, now dope. That is, if Bobo was still working for Kalecki. He said not, and I believed him. I thought Bobo was too simple to try to deceive anybody. I'm not so sure now."

We both stared at the body a bit, then walked down the street a way by ourselves. I happened to think of something.

"Pat."

"Uh-huh."

"Remember when Kalecki was shot at in his home? When he tried to put the finger on me?"

"Yeah. What of it?"

"It was the killer's gun. The killer we want fired that shot. Why? Can you make anything out of it? Even then Kalecki was on the spot for something and he moved to town for his own protection. That's what we want, the answer to the question of why he was shot at."

"That's going to take some doing, Mike. The only ones that can tell us are dead."

I gave him a grin. "No. There's still someone. The killer. He knows why. Have you anything to do right now?"

"Nothing I can't put off. This case will be in Daly's hands for a while. Why?"

I took his arm and walked him around the block to my car. We got in and headed toward my apartment.

The mailman was just coming out when we got there. I opened my box and drew out the envelope I addressed to myself at the college and ripped it open. I explained to Pat I had to get the piece of charred evidence out of the hands of those hick cops while I could and he agreed that I did it right.

Pat knew the ropes. He put in three phone calls and when we reached the bank a guard ushered us into the office of the president. By that time he had already received the court order by phone to permit us to inspect the box listed on the slip.

It was there, all of it. Evidence enough to hang George Kalecki a dozen times over. I was really grateful now that I had put a slug into him. The guy was a rat, all right. He had his fingers in more than I had suspected. There were photostats of checks, letters, a few original documents, and plenty of material to indict George Kalecki for every vice charge there was, including a few new ones.

But nothing else. Where George had gone there was no need for a court. Hal Kines had tied him up in a knot with both ends leading to the hot squat if he had tried to make a break.

Pat ran over the stuff twice, then scooped them all into a large envelope, signed for it and left. Outside I asked, "What are you going to do with the junk?"

"Go over it carefully. Maybe I can trace these checks even though they are made out to cash and don't show the signature on the reverse side. How about you?"

"Might as well go home like I planned. Why, got something else?"

Pat laughed. "We'll see. I had the idea you might be holding out on me, so I wasn't going to tell you this, but since you're still playing it square I'll let you in on something."

He took a pad from his pocket and flipped it open. "Here's some names. See if you know anything about them."

Pat cleared his throat.

"Henry Strebhouse, Carmen Silby, Thelma B. Duval, Virginia R. Reims, Conrad Stevens." Pat stopped and waited, looking at me expectantly.

"Strebhouse and Stevens spent a stretch in the big house," I said. "I don't know the others. Think I saw the Duval girl's name in the society columns once."

"You did. Well, you're not much help, so I'll tell you. Each one of these people is in city or private sanitariums. Dope fiends."

"That's nice," I mused. "How did it get out?"

"Vice squad reported it."

"Yeah. I know they've been on something like that, but it's funny it didn't reach the papers. Oh, I get it. They haven't found the source yet, huh? What is it?"

Pat gave me a wry grin. "That's what Daly would like to know. None of them will reveal it. Not even under threat of imprisonment. Unfortunately for us, some of them have connections too high up for us to try to extract information the hard way. We did get this, though, the stuff was delivered to them via a half-witted little guy who didn't know from nothing."

I let my breath go out hard. "Bobo!"

"Exactly. They'll be able to identify him—if they will. Maybe his death will make them clam up even tighter."

"Damn," I said softly, "and while they're under treatment we can't push them. Our hands are tied very neatly. There's a tie-up, Pat, there has to be. Look how closely all this is connected. At first glance it seems to be loose as hell, but it's not. Bobo and Kalecki . . . Hal and Kalecki . . . Hal and Eileen . . . Eileen and Jack. Either we've run into an outfit that had a lot of irons in the fire or else it was a chain reaction. Jack started it going and the killer knocked him off, but the killer had to cover up something else. From then on it was a vicious circle. Brother, have we run into something!"

"You're not kidding. And we're standing right in the bottom of the well. Now what?"

"Beats me, Pat. I see a little light now, a few things are falling into place."

"What?"

"I'd rather not say. Just little things. They don't point in any direction except to tell me that the killer has a damn good motive for all this."

"Still racing me, Mike?"

"You can bet your pretty white tail on that! I think we're in the home stretch, but the track is muddy now and bogging us down.

We'll have to plod through it to firmer ground before we can start whipping it up." I grinned at him. "You won't beat me out, Pat."

"What do you bet?"

"A steak dinner."

"Taken."

I left him then. He grabbed a cab back to the office and I went up to my apartment. When I took off my pants I felt for my wallet. It was gone. That was nice. Had two hundred berries in my billfold and I couldn't afford to lose it. I put my pants back on and went down to the car. Not there, either. I thought. I might have dropped it in the barber shop, but I paid that bill with change I had in my side pocket. Damn.

I climbed back in the car and turned it over, then headed south to Charlotte's apartment. The lobby door was open and I walked up. I rang the bell twice, but no one answered. Someone was inside, though, and I could hear a voice singing *Swanee River*. I pounded on the door and Kathy opened it up.

"What's the matter," I asked her, "doesn't the bell ring anymore?"

"Sho' nuff, Mistah Hammah. Ah think so. Come in. Come in."

When I walked in the door Charlotte came running out to meet me. She had on a stained smock and a pair of rubber gloves. "Hey, honey," she smiled at me. "You sure made that trip fast. Goody, goody, goody." She threw her arms around me and tilted her head for a kiss. Kathy stood there watching, her teeth flashing whitely in her mouth.

"Go 'way," I grinned. Kathy turned her back so I could kiss her boss. Charlotte sighed and laid her head against my chest.

"Going to stay now?"

"Nope."

"Oh . . . why? You just got here."

"I came to get my wallet." I walked over to the sofa with her and ran my hand down behind the cushions. I found it. The darn thing had slipped out of my hip pocket while I was asleep and stuck there.

"Now I suppose you're going to accuse me of stealing all your money," Charlotte pouted.

"Idiot." I kissed the top of her blond head. "What are you doing in this outfit?" I fingered the smock.

"Developing pictures. Want to see them?" She led me to her darkroom and turned out the lights. As she did so, a red glow came from the shield over the sink. Charlotte put some films in the developer, and in a few moments printed up a pic of a guy sitting in a chair, hands glued to the metal arms, and a strained expression on his face. She flicked the overhead on and looked over the photo.

"Who's this?"

"A clinical patient. As a matter of fact, that is one that Hal Kines had released from the charity ward of the city hospital to undergo treatment in our clinic."

"What's the matter with him? The guy looks scared to death."

"He's in a state of what is commonly known as hypnosis. Actually there's nothing more to it than inducing in the patient a sense of relaxation and confidence. In this case, the patient was a confirmed kleptomaniac. It wasn't found out until he was admitted to the city ward after being found nearly dead of starvation on the streets.

"When we got to the bottom of his mental status, we found that in childhood he had been deprived of everything and had to steal to get what he wanted. Through a friend, I got him a job and explained why he had been like that. Once understanding his condition, he was able to overcome it. Now he's doing quite well."

I put the pic back in a rack and looked the place over. She had certainly spent enough fixing up the darkroom. I saw where I was going to have to earn more than I did to support a wife who had such a lavish hobby.

Charlotte must have read my mind. "After we're married," she smiled, "I'll give all this up and have my pictures developed at the corner drugstore."

"Naw, we'll do all right." She grabbed me and hung on. I kissed her so hard I hurt my mouth this time. It was a wonder she could breathe, I held her so tightly.

We walked to the door arm in arm. "What about tonight, Mike? Where will we go?"

"I don't know. To the movies, maybe."

"Swell, I'd like that." I opened the door. When I did I pointed to the chime behind it. "How come it doesn't ring anymore?"

"Oh, phooey." Charlotte poked under the rug with her toe. "Kathy has been using the vacuum in here again. She always knocks out the plug." I bent down and stuck it back in the socket.

"See you about eight, kitten," I said as I left. She waited until I was nearly out of sight down the stairs, then blew me a kiss and shut the door.

chapter 12

My tailor had a fit when he saw the bullet hole in my coat. I guess he was afraid he was coming close to losing a good customer. He pleaded with me to be careful, then told me he'd have the cloth rewoven by next week. I picked up my other suit and went home.

The phone was ringing when I opened the door. I dropped the suit over the back of a chair and grabbed the receiver. It was Pat.

"I just got a report on the bullet that killed Bobo Hopper, Mike."

"Go on." I was all excited now.

"Same one."

"That does it, Pat. Anything else?"

"Yeah, I have Kalecki's gun here, too. The bullet doesn't fit except with the ones he let loose at you. We traced the serial number and it was sold down South. It went through two more hands and wound up in a pawnshop on Third Avenue where it went to a guy named George K. Masters."

So that was how George got the gun. No wonder there was no record of it before. Kalecki was his middle, and probably a family, name. I thanked Pat and hung up. Now why the hell would Kalecki be using that name? Not unless he was liable to be traced through his real one for a crime committed some time ago. At any rate, the question would have to remain unanswered unless Pat could make some sense out of the evidence we found in the safe-deposit box. You can't prosecute a corpse.

After I ate, I showered and was getting dressed when the phone went off again. This time it was Myrna. She wanted me to pick her up earlier, if I could, tomorrow morning. That was all right with me and I told her so. She still sounded pretty bad and I was glad to do what I could to help her out. Maybe the ride into the country would do her good. Poor kid, she needed something to cheer her up. The only thing that had me worried was that she might try going back on the junk again to get Jack's death out of her mind. She was a smart girl. There were other ways. Some day she would settle down with a nice fellow and Jack would be but a memory. That's the way nature made us. Maybe it's best.

Charlotte met me in front of the apartment house. When she saw me coming she tapped her foot impatiently as though she had been waiting an hour. "Mike," she said fiercely, "you're late. A whole five minutes. Explain."

"Don't beat me with that whip," I laughed. "I got held up in traffic."

"A likely excuse. I bet you were trying to see what makes a nymphomaniac tick again." She was a little devil.

"Shut up and climb in. We'll never get a seat in the show otherwise."

"Where are we going?"

"I'm in the mood for a good 'who-dun-it' if you are. Maybe I can pick up something new in detecting techniques."

"Swell. Let's go, Macduff."

We finally found a small theater along the stem that didn't have a line outside a mile long, and we sat through two and a half hours of a fantastic murder mystery that had more holes in it than a piece of swiss cheese, and a Western that moved as slowly as the Long Island Rail Road during a snowstorm.

When we got out I thought I had blisters on my butt. Charlotte suggested having a sandwich, so we stopped in a dog wagon for poached eggs on toast, then moved on down to a bar for a drink. I ordered beer, and when Charlotte did the same I raised my eyebrows.

"Go ahead, get what you want. I got dough."

She giggled. "Silly, I like beer. Always have."

"Well, glad to hear it. I can't make you out. An expensive hobby, but you drink beer. Maybe you aren't going to be so hard to keep after all."

"Oh, if it comes to a pinch, I can always go back to work."

"Nothing doing. No wife of mine is going to work. I want her at home where I know where she is."

Charlotte laid her beer down and looked at me wickedly. "Has it ever occurred to you that you've never even proposed to me? How do you know I'll have you?"

"Okay, minx," I said. I took her hand in mine and raised it to my lips. "Will you marry me?"

She started to laugh, but tears came into her eyes and she pushed her face against my shoulder. "Oh, Mike, yes. Yes. I love you so much."

"I love you, too, kitten. Now drink your drink. Tomorrow night at the twins' place we'll duck the crowd and make some plans."

"Kiss me."

A couple of wise guys were watching me leeringly. I didn't care. I kissed her easy like.

"When do I get my ring?" she wanted to know.

"Soon. I have a few checks coming in this week or next and we can go down to Tiffany's and pick one up. How's that?"

"Wonderful, Mike, wonderful. I'm so happy."

We finished the beer, had another, then started out. The pair of wise guys threw me a "hey, hey" as I passed. I dropped Charlotte's arm for a second, then put my hands on each side of their heads and brought them together with a clunk like a couple of gourds. Both the guys were sitting upright on their stools. In the mirror I could see their eyes. They looked like four agate marbles. The bartender was watching me, his mouth open. I waved to him and took Charlotte out. Behind me the two guys fell off their stools and hit the deck like wet rags.

"My protector." She squeezed my arm.

"Aw shadup," I grinned. I felt pretty good right then.

Kathy was sleeping, so we tiptoed in. Charlotte put her hand over the chime to stop its reverberations, but even then we heard the maid stop snoring. She must have gone over on her back again because the snoring resumed.

She took off her coat, then asked, "Want a drink?"

"Nope."

"What then?"

"You." The next second she was in my arms, kissing me. Her breasts were pulsating with passion. I held her as closely as I could.

"Tell me, Mike."

"I love you." She kissed me again. I pushed her away and picked up my hat.

"Enough, darling," I said. "After all, I'm only a man. One more kiss like that and I won't be able to wait until after we're married." She grinned and threw herself at me for that kiss, but I held her off.

"Please, Mike?"

"No."

"Then let's get married right away. Tomorrow."

I had to smile. She was so damn adorable. "Not tomorrow, but very soon, honey, I can't hold out much longer."

She held the chime while I opened the door. I kissed her lightly and slipped out. I could see where I wouldn't get much sleep that night. When Velda heard about this she'd throw the roof at me. I hated to tell her.

My alarm went off at six. I slapped the button down to stop the racket, then sat up and stretched. When I looked out the window the sun was shining—a beautiful day. A half-empty bottle of beer was on the night table and I took a swallow. It was as flat as a tabletop mesa.

After a shower I threw a robe around me and dug in the pantry for something to eat. The only box of cereal had teeth marks in it where a mouse had beaten me to it, so I opened a sack of potatoes and onions and stripped them into a pan of grease and let the whole mess cook while I made coffee.

I burned the potatoes, but they tasted good just the same. Even my coffee was agreeable. This time next month I'd be eating across the table from a gorgeous blonde. What a wife she was going to make!

Myrna was up when I called her. She said she'd be ready at eight and reminded me not to be late. I promised her I wouldn't, then buzzed Charlotte.

"Hello, lazy," I yawned.

"You don't sound so bright yourself this time of the morning."

"Well, I am. What are you doing?"

"Trying to get some sleep. After the state you left me in last night I didn't close my eyes for three hours. I lay in bed wide awake."

That made me feel good. "I know what you mean. What time will you be at the Bellemy place?"

"Still early in the evening unless I can break away sooner. At least I'll be there for the game. Who is it that's playing?"

"I forget. A couple of fancy hot shots that Mary and Esther imported. I'll be waiting for you to show up, so make it snappy."

"Okay, darling." She kissed me over the phone and I gave her one back before I hung up.

Velda wouldn't be in the office yet, so I called her at home. When she answered I could hear a background of bacon sizzling on the fire. "Hello, Velda, Mike."

172

"Hey, what are you doing up so early?"

"I have an important date."

"Anything to do with the case?"

"Er . . . it may have, but I'm not sure. I can't afford to miss it. If Pat calls, tell him I can be reached at the home of the Misses Bellemy. He has their number."

Velda didn't answer at first. I knew she was trying to figure out what I was up to. "All right," she said finally. "Just watch what you're doing. Anything I can take care of while you're gone?"

"No, guess not."

"By the way, how long are you going to be gone this time?"

"Maybe until Monday, maybe not."

"Very well, see you, Mike. So long."

I threw her a quick so long and put the phone on its chocks. Oh, how I hated to tell Velda about Charlotte! If only she wouldn't cry. What the hell, that's life. Velda just missed. If Charlotte hadn't come along I would have tied up with her. I used to feel like I wanted to, but never had time. Oh, well.

Myrna was dressed and ready when I arrived. She had packed a bag and I took it down to the car. She didn't look too good. There were still dark spots under her eyes and her cheekbones were a little too prominent. She had bought a new dress for the occasion, a nice flowered print, and under the light blue of the wool coat it made her face look lovely, that is, unless you looked too closely.

I didn't want to mention Jack at all, so we talked about the day and anything trivial that came up. I knew she had seen the front-page headlines about me knocking off Kalecki, but she avoided the subject.

It was a nice day. Out of the city the roads were fairly empty and we rolled along at a conservative fifty. That way I didn't have to bother about the highway patrol. We passed a few open lots where the kids were getting in an early ball game. I saw tears come into Myrna's eyes when we passed some small cottages. I winced. She was taking it hard.

Gradually I led the conversation around to the tennis match that night and got her mind off what she was thinking. It wasn't long afterward that we pulled into the private drive of the Bellemy estate. I thought we were early, but there were two dozen others there before us. A row of cars ran along the side of the mansion and one of the twins came out to meet us. I didn't know which one it was until she said, "Hello, sissy."

"Hello, Mary," I said through a smile. She had on a halter and a pair of shorts that left nothing to the imagination. Both pieces were so tight every line of her body showed through and she knew it. I couldn't get my eyes off her legs, and walking up to the house she kept brushing against me.

That had to cease. I shifted Myrna's grip over to keep a barrier between us, and Mary broke out into a giggle. At the house she turned Myrna over to a maid, then turned to me. "Didn't you bring some sport clothes along?"

"Yup. But all the sports I intend to indulge in will be done at the bar."

"Nuts. Go get in a pair of slacks. There's a golf game to be held behind the house and a lot of the kids are looking for partners for a tennis game."

"For Pete's sake, I'm no athlete."

Mary stood off a few feet and looked me over from top to bottom. "You look like an athlete if I ever saw one."

"What kind?" I joked.

"A bed athlete." Her eyes said that she wasn't joking.

She walked back to the car with me to get my clothes. When we got in the house she showed me to a room, an oversized thing with a huge four-poster smack in the middle of it.

Mary couldn't wait until I closed the door. She flung herself at me and opened her mouth. Hell, I couldn't disappoint the hostess, so I kissed her.

"Now scram while I get dressed," I told her.

Her mouth went into a pout. "Why?"

"Look," I tried to be convincing, "I don't get undressed in front of women."

"Since when?" she asked impishly.

"It was dark then," I told her. "Besides, it's too early for that."

I got another one of those sexy smiles. Her eyes were begging me to undress her. "Okay . . . sissy." She closed the door behind her and I heard that deep-throated laugh.

The gang outside was making a racket and I poked my head out the window to see what was up. Directly beneath me two underweight males were having a hair-pulling match while four others egged them on. What a place. The two boys hit the dirt together and followed by a slap or two. I grinned. A couple of pansies trying to decide who would be Queen of the May. I drew a pitcher of water from the sink and let it go on their blond heads.

That ended the fight. They both let out a falsetto scream and got up running. The gang saw me and howled. It was a good gag.

Mary met me downstairs. She was lounging against the porch railing smoking a cigarette. I came out in slacks and a sweatshirt and tossed her a hello. Myrna joined us at the same time swinging a tennis racket against her legs. I could see that Mary was disappointed at not getting me alone. The three of us walked across the lawn to the courts with Mary hanging on to my arm. Before we quite reached there another edition of her stepped out of a group of players and waved to us. Esther Bellemy.

She was another to make your mouth drool. She recognized me immediately and offered a firm handshake. Her manner was cool and reserved. I saw what Charlotte meant when she said Esther wasn't like her sister. However, there seemed to be no resentment or jealousy. Esther had her admirers, too. We were introduced all around to a lot of people whose names I forgot as soon as I met them, and Mary carted me off to a vacant court for a game of singles.

Tennis wasn't in my line, she found out. After a hectic ten minutes I had batted the balls over the fence and we gathered them up and put them in a box and laid the rackets down. Mary sat on a bench beside me with her brown legs stuck out in front of her while I cooled off.

"Why are we wasting time out here, Mike? Your room is so much nicer."

Some dame. "You rush things, Mary. Why aren't you more like your sister?"

She gave me a short laugh. "Maybe I am."

"How do you mean?"

"Oh, nothing, I guess. But Esther keeps her eyes open, too. She's no virgin."

"How do you know?"

Mary giggled and folded her knees under her hands. "She keeps a diary."

"I bet yours is a lot thicker," I said.

"Uh-huh, lots."

I took her hand and pulled her from the bench. "Come on, show me where the bar is."

We took a flagstone path back to the house and entered through a pair of French windows. The bar was built off a trophy room that was well packed with cups and medals, decorated with live-oak paneling and blown-up photographs of the Bellemy sisters winning everything from a golf game to a ski jump. They certainly were an active pair. The curious thing about it was that they didn't like publicity. I wondered where the rumor started that they were looking for husbands. Husbands that would satisfy, maybe.

I guess Mary gave me up as hopeless for a while. She left me with a colored bartender who sat at the end of the thirty-foot bar reading a stack of comic magazines, getting up only long enough to pour me a fresh drink every time I emptied my glass.

Several times I had company, but not for long. Myrna came in once, then left after a few pleasant words. Some other tootsies tried their hand at making a strange face but were dragged off by their boyfriends who chased them into the bar. One of the pansies I doused did his bit, too, and all it took to get him out was a strong hand on the seat of his shorts and another around his neck. The whole deal was getting very monotonous. I wished Charlotte would get here. I thought I'd have a nice time with Mary, but compared to Charlotte she was a flop. Mary only had sex. Charlotte had that—plus a lot more.

I managed to sneak out without the bartender seeing me and found my room. There I changed back to my street clothes, patted old junior under my arm and lay down on the bed. Now I felt normal.

The drinks did more to me than I thought. I didn't pass out, I simply fell asleep, but quick. The next thing I knew someone was shaking me and I looked up into the prettiest face in the world. Before my eyes were all the way open, Charlotte kissed me, then mussed my hair.

"Is this the way you greet me? I thought you'd be at the gate waiting for me with open arms."

"Hello, beautiful," I said.

I pulled her down on the bed and kissed her. "What time is it?" She looked at her watch.

"Seven-thirty."

"Holy cow! I slept the whole day out practically!"

"I'll say you have. Now get dressed and come downstairs for dinner. I want to see Myrna."

We got up and I saw her to the door, then washed my face and tried to smooth the wrinkles out of my coat. When I thought I was presentable enough I went downstairs. Mary saw me and waved me over. "You're sitting by me tonight," she told me.

The crowd was beginning to file in and I found the place card with my name on it. Charlotte was sitting directly opposite me at any rate. I felt much better at that. The two of them ought to be fun unless Mary started playing kneesy under the table.

Charlotte sat down with a smile and Myrna was next to her. Through the appetizer they spoke to each other earnestly, laughing occasionally over some private joke.

I glanced down the table to see if there was anyone I knew. One face seemed fairly familiar, although I couldn't place it. He was a short, skinny guy, dressed in a dark grey flannel. His only conversation was with the heavy-set woman opposite him. There was so much chatter at the table I couldn't get a line on what they were talking about, but I saw him sneak a few side glances my way.

He happened to turn his full face toward me for a moment, then I recognized him. He was one of the men I had seen going into Madam June's call house the night of the raid.

I nudged Mary and she quit talking to the guy on her other side long enough to look my way. "Who's the squirt down at the end?" I asked, motioning with my fork.

Mary picked him out and said, "Why, that's Harmon Wilder, our attorney. He's the one who invests our money for us. Why?"

"Just curious. I thought I recognized him."

"You should. He used to be one of the best criminal lawyers in the country before he gave it up for a private practice in something less sensational."

I said, "Oh," then returned to my food. Charlotte had found my foot under the table and tapped it with her toe. Behind the table the lawn was moon-lit—a perfect night. I'd be glad when supper was over.

Mary tried me out in conversation all too suggestive. I saw Charlotte give her a glance that was full of fire, winked, then cut Mary off pretty sharply. She sort of got the idea that something was up between me and Charlotte and whispered into my ear. "I'll get you tonight, big stuff—after she's gone."

She yelped when I stuck my elbow in her ribs.

Dinner ended when one of the fruits fell out of his chair at the table's end. Right after that there was a lot of noise and the two tennis players who were to be featured in the game that night stood up and toasted success to each other with glasses of milk.

I managed to get through to Charlotte and took Myrna and her out to the courts together. A lot of cars were driving up, probably some neighbors invited just for the game. The floodlights had been turned on over the sunbaked clay, and bleacher seats had been erected sometime during the latter part of the afternoon while I was asleep.

There was a general scramble for seats and we missed. Charlotte and Myrna spread their handkerchiefs down on the grass along the border of the playing field and we waited while the crowd got six deep behind us. I had never seen a real tennis game, but from what I had seen, I didn't think there were that many people who liked the game.

There were announcements over a portable loudspeaker and the players took their places. Then they went into action. I had more fun watching the spectators' heads going back and forth like a bunch of monkeys on sticks than I did the game itself.

These boys were pretty good. They worked up a terrific sweat but they kept after that ball, running themselves ragged. Occasionally there would be a spectacular play and the crowd would let out a cheer. On a high bench, the referee announced the score.

Myrna kept pressing her hand to her head, then between sets she excused herself to Charlotte and me saying that she wanted to go to the cloakroom and get an aspirin.

No sooner had she left when Mary plunked herself down in the same spot beside me and started her routine. I waited for Charlotte to start something, but she merely smiled grimly and let me fight it out myself.

Mary tapped her on the shoulder. "Can I borrow your man a few minutes? I want him to meet some people."

"Sure, go ahead." Charlotte winked gaily at me and made believe she was pouting, but she knew she had me. From now on Charlotte had nothing to worry about. Just the same I felt like throttling Mary. Just sitting there had been nice.

We wormed out through the gang who had moved up to take new places and stretch themselves between sets. Mary took me around to the other side, then started walking toward the woods.

"Where're the people you wanted me to meet?" I asked.

Her hand groped for mine in the darkness. "Don't be silly," she answered. "I just want you to myself for a while."

"Look, Mary," I explained, "it's no good. The other night was a mistake. Charlotte and I are engaged. I can't be fooling around with you. It isn't fair to either of you."

She tucked her arm under mine. "Oh, but you don't have to marry me. I don't want that. It takes all the fun out of it."

What was I going to do with a woman like that? "Listen," I told her, "you're a nice kid and I like you a lot, but you are a serious complication to me."

She let my arm go. We were under a tree now, and it was pitch black. I could barely see the outline of her face. The moon which not so long ago had been out in full brilliance had disappeared behind a cloud. I kept talking to her, trying to dissuade her from putting a line on me, but she didn't answer. She hummed snatches from a tune I heard her breathing in the darkness, but that was all.

When I had about exhausted myself, she said, "Will you kiss me just once more if I promise to let you alone?"

I breathed a little easier. "Sure, honey. Just one more kiss."

Then I stretched out my arms to hold her to kiss, and I got the shock of my life. The little devil had taken off all her clothes in the darkness.

That kiss was like molten lava. I couldn't push her away, nor did I want to now. She clung to me like a shadow, squirming and pulling at me. The sound of the crowd cheering the game a hundred yards away dimmed to nothingness and all I could hear was the roaring in my ears.

The game was almost over when we got back. I scrubbed the lipstick away from my mouth and dusted off my clothes. Mary saw her sister and was gracious enough to let me alone for a while, so while I still had the chance I skirted the crowd and tried to find Charlotte. She was where I had left her, only she had gotten tired of sitting down. She and a tall youngster were splitting a coke together. That made me mad.

Hell, I was a fine one to be pulling a jealousy stunt after what I just did. I called to her and she came back to me. "Where have you been?"

"Fighting," I lied, "fighting for my honor."

"You look it. How did you make out? Or shouldn't I ask?"

"I did it all right. It took time though. You been here all the time?"

"Yep. Just like a good little wife, I sit home while my husband is out with other women," she laughed.

The shout that ended the tennis game came simultaneously with the scream from the house. That scream stifled any cheer that might have been given. It rang out in the night again and again, then dwindled off to a low moan.

I dropped Charlotte's hand and ran for the house. The colored bartender was standing in the doorway as white as a sheet. He could hardly talk. He pointed up the stairs and I took them two at a time.

The first floor opened on the cloakroom, an affair as big as a small ballroom. The maid was huddled on the floor, out like a light. Beyond her was Myrna, a bullet hole clean through her chest. She still had her hands clutched futilely against her breasts as though to protect herself.

I felt her pulse. She was dead.

Downstairs the crowd was pounding across the lawn. I shouted to the colored boy to shut the doors, then grabbed the phone and got the gatekeeper. I told him to close the gates and not let anyone out, hung up, and dashed downstairs. I picked out three men in overalls whom I had taken for gardeners and asked them who they were.

"Gardener," one said. The other was a handyman on the estate and the third was his helper.

"Got any guns around here?" They nodded. "Six shotguns and a 30.30 in the library," the handyman said.

"Then get 'em," I ordered. "There's been a murder upstairs and the killer is someplace on the grounds. Patrol the estate and shoot anybody you see trying to get away. Understand?"

The gardener started to argue, but when I pulled my badge on him, he and the others took off for the library, got the guns, returned a minute later and shot out the door.

The crowd was gathered in front. I stepped outside and held up my hand for silence. When I told them what had happened there were a few screams, a lot of nervous talk, and everyone in general had the jitters.

I held up my hand again. "For your own benefit you had better not try to leave. There are men posted with orders to shoot if anyone tries to run for it. If you are wise, you'll find someone who was standing near by you during the game and have an alibi ready. Only don't try to dummy one because it won't work. Stay here on the porch where you can be reached at a moment's notice."

Charlotte came in the door, her face white, and asked, "Who was it, Mike?"

"Myrna. The kid has nothing to worry about anymore. She's dead. And I have the killer right under my nose someplace."

"Can I do something, Mike?"

"Yeah. Get the Bellemy sisters and bring them to me."

When she went for them I called for the colored boy. Shaking like a leaf he came over to me. "Who came in here?"

"I don' see nobody, boss. I see one girl come in. I never see her come out 'cause she's daid upstairs."

"Were you here all the time?"

"Yassuh. All de time. I watch for the folks to come in heah for a drink. Then I goes to the bar."

"What about the back door?"

"It's locked, boss. Only way is in through heah. Don' nobody come in 'cept de girl. She's daid."

"Quit saying that over and over," I stormed. "Just answer my questions. Did you leave here for a second?"

"Nosuh, boss, not hardly a second."

"What's not hardly?"

The darky looked scared. He was afraid to commit himself one way or another. "Come on, speak up."

"I got me a drink once, boss. Just beer, that's all. Don't tell Miss Bellemy."

"Damn," I said. That minute was time enough to let a murderer in here.

"How quickly did you come back? Wait a minute. Go in there and get a beer. Let me see how long it took you." The darky shuffled off while I timed him. Fifteen seconds later he was back with a bottle in his hand.

"Did you do it that fast before? Think now. Did you drink it here or in there?"

"Here, boss," he said simply, pointing to an empty bottle on the floor. I yelled to him not to move, then ran for the back of the house. The place was built in two sections, this part an addition to the other. The only way in was through the French windows to the bar and the back door, or the one connecting door to the other section. The windows were bolted. So was the back door. The twin doors between the two sections of the building were firmly in place and locked. I looked for other possible entries, but there were none. If that were so I could still have the killer trapped somewhere inside.

Quickly, I raced up the stairs. The maid was recovering and I helped her to her feet. She was pasty-faced and breathing hard, so I sat her down on the top step as Charlotte came in with the twins.

The maid was in no condition to answer questions. I shouted down to Charlotte to call Pat Chambers as fast as she could and get him up here. He could call the local cops later. Mary and Esther came up and took the maid out of my hands and half carried her downstairs to a chair.

I went into the murder room and closed the door after me. I didn't worry about fingerprints. My killer never left any.

Myrna had on her blue coat, though I couldn't see why. The night was far too warm for it. She lay in front of a full-length mirror, doubled up. I looked closely at the wound. Another .45. The killer's gun. I was bent down on my knees looking for the bullet when I noticed the stuff on the rug. A white powder. Around it the nap of the carpet had been ruffled as though someone had tried to scoop it up. I took an envelope from my pocket and got some of the grains inside. I felt the body. It was still warm. But then, at this temperature, *rigor mortis* wouldn't set in until late.

Myrna's hands were clenched together so tightly I had difficulty working my fingers under hers. She had clawed at her coat trying to hold the wound, and fibers of wool were caught under her fingernails. She had died hard, but fast. Death was merciful.

I felt under the coat, and there in the folds of the cloth was the bullet, a .45. I had my killer here. All I had to do was find him. Why he should kill Myrna was beyond me. She was as far out of the case as I was. The motive. The motive. What the hell kind of a motive was it that ate into so many people? The people the killer reached out and touched had nothing to give. They were all so different.

Jack, yes. I could see where he'd got mixed up in murder, but Myrna, no. Look at Bobo. Nothing could make me believe he was part of the picture. Where was motive there? Dope, he had been delivering it. But the connection. He never lived long enough to tell where he got the package or to whom it was going.

I shut the door softly behind me out of respect for the dead. Esther Bellemy had the maid in a chair at the foot of the stairs trying to comfort her. Mary was pouring herself a stiff whisky, her hands trembling. This hit her hard, whereas Esther was well composed. Charlotte came in with a cold compress and held it against the maid's head.

"Can she talk yet?" I asked Charlotte.

"Yes, I think so. Just be easy with her."

I knelt in front of the maid and patted her hand. "Feel better?" She nodded. "Good, I just want to ask you a few questions, then you can lie down. Did you see anyone come or go?"

"No. I—I was in the back of the house cleaning up."

"Did you hear a shot?"

Another negative.

I called over to the colored man. "What about you, hear anything?"

"Nosuh, I don' heah nuthin'."

If neither had heard the shot, then the silencer must still be on the .45. And if the killer had it around, we'd find it. That kind of a rig is too big to hide.

I went back to the maid. "Why did you go upstairs?"

"To straighten out the clothes. The women had left them all over the bed. That's when I saw the b-body." She buried her face in her hands and sobbed quietly.

"Now, one more thing, did you touch anything?"

"No, I fainted."

"Put her to bed, Charlotte; see if you can find something to make her sleep. She's pretty upset."

Between Charlotte and Esther they half dragged the maid to a bed. Mary Bellemy was pouring one drink after another in her. She wouldn't be standing up much longer. I took the darky aside.

"I'm going upstairs. Don't let anyone in or out unless I say so, you hear? You do and you'll wind up in jail yourself." I didn't have to say anything else. He stammered out a reply that I didn't get, then locked and bolted the front door.

My killer had to be somewhere around. He had to leave through the front door unless he went out an upstairs window. Everything else was locked up tightly. But except for the little bit of time the bartender was away from the door, someone was there. That time had been enough to let the killer in, but not enough to let him back out again. Not without being seen by the bartender, that is. If the darky had seen someone and had been told to keep his mouth shut, I would have known it. I could swear that he was telling the truth. Besides, my killer would have knocked him off as well, and as easily, rather than take the risk of exposure.

From the top of the stairs, the hall crossed like a T. Doors opened off the one side, and each proved to be a guest room. I tried the windows. Locked. I went up and down both ends of the T trying to find where the exit was. Each room I inspected and searched with my rod in my fist, waiting, hoping.

The murder room was the last room I tried. And that's where the killer got out. The window slid up easily, and I looked down fifteen feet to a flagstone walk below. If he had jumped he wouldn't be walking now. The drop was enough to break a leg, especially on those stones. Around the building and directly under the window ran a narrow ledge. It projected out about eight inches from the wall and was clean of dust or dirt on both sides of the window. I lit a match and looked for heel marks in the concrete of the ledge, but there were none. Not a mark. This was enough to drive me nuts.

Even the eight inches wasn't enough to walk across on barefaced brick. I tried it. I got out on the ledge and tried first to walk along with my face to the wall, then with my back to it. In both cases I almost took a spill. It would take a real athlete to cross that. Someone who was part cat.

Inside the room, I pulled the window down and went back to the hall. At either end a window overlooked the grounds. I didn't see it at first, but when I stuck my head out there was a fire-escape ladder built into the wall adjacent to the window. Oh, how pretty if it could be done. The killer strikes, then out the window to the ledge, and around to the fire escape. Now I had an acrobat on my hands. Swell, more headaches.

I went downstairs and took the bottle away from Mary in time to salvage a drink from the wreckage and ease her into a chair. She was dead drunk.

A half hour later I had still gotten nowhere when I heard the pounding of feet outside and told the darky to open up.

Pat and his staff walked in escorted by some county police. How that guy could get around the red tape of city limitations and restrictions was beyond me. He went upstairs at once, listening as I gave him the details.

I finished as he was bent over the body. The county coroner bustled in, declared the girl officially dead and made out a report. "How long since she died?" Pat asked.

The coroner hemmed and hawed, then said, "Roughly, about two hours. This warm weather makes it difficult to place the time exactly. Tell better after an autopsy."

Two hours was close enough. It had happened while I was out in the bushes with Mary Bellemy.

Pat asked me, "Everyone here?"

"Guess so. Better get a guest list from Esther and check up. I posted guards around the wall and at the gate."

"Okay, come on downstairs."

Pat herded the entire group of them into the main room in the other section of the building. He had them packed in like sardines. Esther gave him a guest list and he read off names. As each one heard his name called, he sat on the floor. The detectives watched closely to be sure none of them moved until they were supposed to. Half the group was seated when Pat called out "Harmon Wilder."

No answer. He tried again, "Harmon Wilder." Still no answer. My little friend had vanished. Pat nodded to a detective who moved to a phone. The manhunt was on.

Six names later Pat sang out, "Charles Sherman." He called it three more times and no one answered. That was a name I hadn't heard before. I walked over to Esther.

"Who is this Sherman?"

"Mr. Wilder's assistant. He was here during the game. I saw him."

"Well, he's not here now."

I relayed the information to Pat and another name went out to call cars and police stations. Pat read down the list; when he was done there were still twenty standees. Gate crashers. You find them everywhere. The total number crammed into that house was over two hundred and fifty persons.

Pat assigned a certain number to each detective and some to me. Because I had been on the scene he let me take all the servants, the twins, Charlotte, and ten others from the party. Pat took the gate crashers for himself. As soon as he gave out the list, he quieted the assembly and cleared his throat.

"Everyone present here is under suspicion for murder," he said. "Naturally, I know that you all couldn't have done it. You are to report to each of my men as your name is called. They will speak to you separately. What we want is your alibi, whom you were with at the game, or wherever you were"—he checked his watch—"two hours and fifty minutes ago. If you can vouch for someone standing near you, do it. By doing so you are only insuring your own alibi. I want the truth. Nothing else. We will catch you if you try falsifying your statements. That is all."

I collected my group and took them out on the porch. The household help I disposed of first. They had all been together and spoke for one another. The ten new faces assured me that they had been with certain parties and I took their statements. Mary had been with me, so she was out. Esther had been beside the referee's stand most of the time and this was corroborated by the rest. I shooed them away, Esther leading her still half-out sister. I saved Charlotte until last so we could have the porch together.

"Now you, kitten," I said. "Where were you?"

"You have a nerve," she said laughingly. "Right where you left me."

"Aw, don't get sore, baby, I was trapped."

I kissed her and she said, "After that, all is forgiven. Now I'll tell you where I was. Part of the time I was sipping a coke with a nice young gentleman named Fields, and part of the time exchanging witticisms with a rather elderly wolf. I don't know his name, but he was one of those that weren't on the list. He has a spade beard."

I remembered him. I put down "spade beard," no name. Charlotte stayed close to me as we walked back into the room. Pat was picking up the list as his men finished and cross-checking them to see if the stories held water. A couple had the names confused, but they were soon adjusted. When all were in we compared them.

Not a single one was without an alibi. And it didn't seem sensible that Wilder and Sherman should have run off—they had been accounted for, too. Pat and I let out a steady stream of curses without stopping. When we got our breaths Pat instructed his men to get names and addresses of everyone present and told them to inform the guests that they had better stay within reaching distance or else.

He was right. It was practically an impossibility to hold that many people there at once. It looked like we were still following a hopeless trail.

Most of the cars left at once. Pat had a cop handing out the coats since he didn't want anyone messing up the murder room. I went up with Charlotte to get hers. The cop pulled out her blue job with the white wolf collar and I helped her into it.

Mary was still out so I didn't say good-bye to her. Esther was at the door downstairs, as calm as ever, seeing the guests out, even being nice to the ones that didn't belong there.

I shook hands with her and told her I'd see her soon and Charlotte and I left. Instead of driving up, she had taken the train, so we both got into my car and started back.

Neither one of us spoke much. As the miles passed under my wheels I got madder and madder. The circle. It started with Jack and had ended with him. The killer finally got around to Myrna.

It was crazy. The whole pattern was bugs. Now my motive was completely shot to hell. Myrna fitted in nowhere. I heard a sob beside me and caught Charlotte wiping tears from her eyes. That was easy to see. She had taken a liking to Myrna.

I put my arm around her and squeezed. This must seem like a nightmare to her. I was used to death sitting on my doorstep, she wasn't. Maybe when the dragnet brought in Wilder and Sherman there would be an answer to something. People just don't run away for nothing. The outsider. The answer to the question. Could either of them have been the outsider that belonged in the plot? Very possible. It seemed more possible now than ever. Manhunt. The things the cops were best at. Go get them. Don't miss. If they try to run, kill the bastards. I don't care if I don't get them myself, so long as someone does. No glory. Justice.

When I stopped in front of Charlotte's place I had to stop thinking. I looked at my watch. Well after midnight. I opened the door for her.

"Want to come up?"

"Not tonight, darling," I said. "I want to go home and think."

"I understand. Kiss me good night." She held out her face and I kissed her. How I loved that girl. I'd be glad when this was over with and we could get married.

"Will I see you tomorrow?"

I shook my head. "I doubt it. If I can find time I'll call you."

"Please, Mike," she begged, "try to make it. Otherwise I can't see you until Tuesday."

"What's the matter with Monday?" I asked her.

"Esther and Mary are coming back to the city and I promised to have supper with them. Esther is more upset than you realize.

Mary will get over it fast enough, but her sister isn't like that. You know how women are when they get in a spot."

"Okay, baby. If I don't see you tomorrow, I'll give you a call Monday and see you Tuesday. Maybe then we can go get that ring."

This time I gave her a long kiss and watched her disappear into the building. I had some tall thinking to do. Too many had died. I was afraid to let it go further. It had to be now or not at all. I tooled the jalopy back to the garage, parked it and went upstairs to bed.

chapter 13

Sunday was a flop. It opened with the rain splattering against the windows and the alarm shattering my eardrums. I brought my fist down on the clock, swearing at myself because I set it automatically when I didn't have to get up at all.

This was one day when I didn't have to shower or shave. I burned my breakfast as usual and ate it while I was in my underwear. When I was stacking the dishes, I glanced at myself in the mirror, and a dirty, unkempt face glared back at me. On days like this I look my ugliest.

Fortunately, the refrigerator was well stocked with beer. I pulled out two quarts, got a glass from the cabinet, a spare pack of butts, and laid them beside my chair. Then I opened the front door and the papers fell to the floor. Very carefully, I separated the funnies from the pile, threw the news section in the waste basket and began the day.

I tried the radio after that. I tried pacing the floor. Every ashtray was filled to overflowing. Nothing seemed to help. Occasionally I would flop in the chair and put my head in my hands and try to think. But whatever I did, I invariably came up with the same answer. Stymied. Nuts.

Something was trying to get out. I knew it. I could feel it. Way back in the recesses of my mind a little detail was gnawing its way through, screaming to be heard, but the more it gnawed, the greater were the defences erected to prevent its escaping.

Not a hunch. A fact. Some small, trivial fact. What was it? Could it be the answer? Something was bothering me terrifically. I tried some more beer. No. No. No . . . no . . . no . . . no . . . no. The answer wouldn't come. How must our minds be made? So complicated that a detail gets lost in the maze of knowledge. Why? That damn ever-present WHY. There's a why to everything. It was there, but how to bring it out? I tried thinking around the issue, I tried to think through it. I even tried to forget it, but the greater the effort, the more intense the failure.

I never noticed the passage of time. I drank, I ate, it was dark out and I turned the lights on and drank some more. Hours and minutes and seconds. I fought, but lost. So I fought again. One detail. What was it? What was it?

The refrigerator was empty all of a sudden and I fell into bed exhausted. It never broke through. That night I dreamed the killer was laughing at me. A killer whose face I couldn't see. I dreamed that the killer had Jack and Myrna and the rest of them hanging in chains, while I tried in vain to beat my way through a thin partition of glass with a pair of .45s to get to them. The killer was unarmed, laughing fiendishly, as I raved and cursed, but the glass wouldn't break. I never got through.

I awoke with a bad taste in my mouth. I brushed my teeth, but that didn't get rid of the taste. I looked out the window. Monday was no better than the day before. The rain was coming down in buckets. I couldn't stand to be holed up any longer, so I shaved and got dressed, then donned a raincoat and went out to eat. It was twelve then; when I finished it was one. I dropped in a bar and ordered one highball after another. The next time I looked at the clock it was nearly six.

That was when I reached in my pocket for another pack of cigarettes. My hand brushed an envelope. Damn, I could have kicked myself. I asked the bartender where the nearest drugstore was and he directed me around the corner.

The place was about to close, but I made it. I took the envelope out and asked him if he could test an unknown substance for me. The guy agreed reluctantly. Together we shook the stuff on to a piece of paper and he took it into the back. It didn't take long. I was fixing my tie in front of a mirror when he came back. He handed me the envelope with a suspicious glance. On it he had written one word.

Heroin.

I looked in the mirror again. What I saw turned the blood in my veins to liquid ice. I saw my eyes dilate. The mirror. The mirror and that one word. I shoved the envelope into my pocket viciously and handed the druggist a fin.

I couldn't talk. There was a crazy job bubbling inside me that made me go alternately hot and cold. If my throat hadn't been so tight I could have screamed. All this time. Not time wasted, because it had to be this way. Happy, happy. How could I be so happy? I had the WHY, but how could I be so happy? It wasn't right. I beat Pat to it after all. He didn't have the WHY. Only I did.

Now I knew who the killer was.

And I was happy. I walked back to the bar.

I took a last drag on the cigarette and flipped it spinning into the gutter, then turned and walked into the apartment house. Someone made it easy for me by not closing the lobby door tightly. No use taking the elevator, there was still plenty of time. I walked up the stairs wondering what the finale would be like.

The door was locked but I expected that. The second pick I used opened it. Inside, the place was filled with that curious stillness evident in an empty house. There was no need to turn on the lights, I knew the layout well enough. Several pieces of furniture were fixed in my mind. I sat down in a heavy chair set catercorner against the two walls. The leaves of a rubber plant on a table behind the chair brushed against my neck. I pushed them away and slid down into the lushness of the cushions to make myself comfortable, then pulled the .45 from its holster and snapped the safety off.

I waited for the killer.

Yes, Jack, this is it, the end. It took a long time to get around to it, but I did. I know who did it now. Funny, the way things worked out, wasn't it? All the symptoms were backwards. I had the wrong ones figured for it until the slip came. They all make that one slip. That's what the matter is with these cold-blooded killers; they plan, oh, so well. But they have to work all the angles themselves, while we have many heads working the problem out. Yeah, we miss plenty, but eventually someone stumbles on the logical solution. Only this one wasn't logical. It was luck. Remember what I promised you? I'd shoot the killer, Jack, right in the gut where you got it. Right where everyone could see what he had for dinner. Deadly, but he wouldn't die fast. It would take a few minutes. No matter who it turned out to be, Jack, I'd get the killer. No chair, no rope, just the one slug in the gut that would take the breath from the lungs and the life from the body. Not much blood, but I would be able to look at the killer dying at my feet and be glad that I kept my promise to you. A killer should die that way. Hard, nasty. No fanfare except the blast of an unsilenced .45 going off in a small, closed room. Yeah, Jack, no matter whom it turned out to be, that's the way death would come. Just like you got it. I know who did it. In a few minutes the killer will walk in here and see me sitting in this chair. Maybe the killer will try to talk me out of it, maybe even kill again, but I don't kill easy. I know all the angles. Besides, I got a rod in my fist, waiting. Waiting. Before I do it I'll make the killer sweat—and tell me how it happened, to see if I hit it right. Maybe I'll even give the rat a chance to get me. More likely not. I hate too hard and shoot too fast. That's why people say the things about me that they do. That's why the killer would have had to try for me soon. Yes, Jack, it's almost finished. I'm waiting. I'm waiting.

The door opened. The lights flicked on. I was slumped too low in the chair for Charlotte to see me. She took her hat off in front of the wall mirror. Then she saw my legs sticking out. Even under the makeup I could see the color drain out of her face.

(Yes, Jack, Charlotte. Charlotte the beautiful. Charlotte the lovely. Charlotte who loved dogs and walked people's babies in the park. Charlotte whom you wanted to crush in your arms and feel the wetness of her lips. Charlotte of the body that was fire and life and soft velvet and responsiveness. Charlotte the killer.)

She smiled at me. It was hard to tell that it wasn't forced, but I knew it. *She knew I knew it.* And she knew why I was here. The .45 was levelled straight at her stomach.

Her mouth smiled at me, her eyes smiled at me, and she looked pleased, so glad to see me, just as she had always been. She was almost radiant when she spoke. "Mike, darling. Oh, baby, I'm so glad to see you. You didn't call like you promised and I've been worried. How did you get in? Oh, but Kathy is always leaving the door open. She's off tonight." Charlotte started to walk toward me. "And please, Mike, don't clean that awful gun here. It scares me."

"It should," I said.

She stopped a few feet away from me, her face fixed on mine. Her brows creased in a frown. Even her eyes were puzzled. If it were anyone but me they'd never have known she was acting. Christ, she was good! There was no one like her. The play was perfect, and she wrote, directed and acted all the parts. The timing was exact, the strength and character she put into every moment, every expression, every word was a crazy impossibility of perfection. Even now she could make me guess, almost build a doubt in my mind, but I shook my head slowly.

"No good, Charlotte, I know."

Her eyes opened wider. Inside me I smiled to myself. Her mind must have been racing with fear. *She* remembered my promise to Jack. She couldn't forget it. Nobody could, because I'm me and I always keep a promise. And this promise was to get the killer, and she was the killer. And I had promised to shoot the killer in the stomach.

She walked to an end table and picked a cigarette from a box, then lit it with a steady hand. That's when I knew, too, that she had figured an out. I didn't want to tell her that it was a useless out. The gun never left her a second.

"But . . ."

"No," I said, "let me tell you, Charlotte. I was a little slow in catching on, but I got it finally. Yesterday I would have dreaded this, but not now. I'm glad. Happier than I've been in a long time. It was the last kill. They were so different. So damn cold-blooded that I had it figured for a kill-crazy hood or an outsider. You were lucky. Nothing seemed to tie up, there were so many complications. It jumped around from one thing to another, yet every one of those things was part of the same basic motive.

"Jack was a cop. Someone always hates cops. Especially a cop that is getting close to him. But Jack didn't know just who he was getting close to until you held a rod on him and pumped one into his intestines. That was it, wasn't it?"

She looked so pathetic standing there. Twin tears welled up and rolled down her cheeks. So pathetic and so helpless. As though she wanted to stop me, to tell me I was wrong—to show me *how* wrong I was. Her eyes were pools of supplication, begging, pleading. But I went on.

"It was you and Hal at first. No, just you alone. Your profession started it. Oh, you made money enough, but not enough. You are a woman who wanted wealth and power. Not to use it extravagantly, but just to have it. How many times have you gone into the frailty of men and seen their weaknesses? It made you afraid. You no longer had the social instinct of a woman—that of being dependent upon a man. You were afraid, so you found a way to increase your bank account and charge it to business. A way in which you'd never be caught, but a dirty way. The dirtiest way there is—almost."

(The sorrow drifted from her eyes, and there was something else in its stead. It was coming now. I couldn't tell what it was, but it was coming. She stood tall and straight as a martyr, exuding beauty and trust and belief. Her head turned slightly and I saw a sob catch in her throat. Like a soldier. Her stomach was so flat against the belt of her skirt. She let her arms drop simply at her sides, her hands asking to be held, and her lips wanting to silence mine with a kiss. It was coming, but I dared not stop now. I couldn't let her speak or I would never be able to keep my promise.)

"Your clientele. It was wealthy, proud. With your ability and appearance and your constant studies, you were able to draw such a group to you. Yes, you treated them, eased their mental discomfitures—but with drugs. Heroin. You prescribed, and they took your prescription—to become addicts, and you were their only source for the stuff and they had to pay through the nose to get it. Very neat. So awfully neat. Being a doctor, and through your clinic, you could get all the stuff you needed. I don't know how your delivery system worked, but that will come later.

"Then you met Hal Kines. An innocent meeting, but isn't that the way all things start? That's why I had trouble with the answer, it was all so casual. You never suspected him of his true activities, did you? But one day you used him as a subject for an experiment in hypnosis, didn't you? He was a fool to do it, but he had no choice if he wanted to play his role. And while he was under hypnosis you inadvertently brought to light every dirty phase of his life.

"You thought you had him then. You told him what you had discovered and were going to fit him into your plans. But you were fooled. Hal was not a college kid. He was an adult. An adult with a mature, scheming mind, who could figure things out for himself—and he had already caught wise to what you were doing and was going to hold it over *your* head. All you got out of that was a stalemate. Remember the book on your shelf—*Hypnosis as a Treatment for Mental Disorders?* It was well thumbed. I knew you were well versed in that angle, but I never caught on until yesterday."

(She was standing in front of me now. I felt a hot glow go over me as I saw what she was about to do. Her hands came up along her sides pressing her clothes tightly against her skin, then slowly ran under her breasts, cupping them. Her fingers fumbled with the buttons of the blouse, but not for long. They came open—one by one.)

"You and Hal held on tightly, each waiting for the other to make a break, but there was too much of a risk to take to start anything. That's where Jack came in. He was a shrewd one. That guy had a brain. Sure, he helped Hal out of a small jam, but in doing so something aroused his suspicions, and all the while he pretended to be helping Hal with his work he was really investigating him. Jack found out what Hal was up to, and when by accident he met Eileen, she confirmed it. Jack knew about the show through her, and since Hal was the brains of the outfit, knew, too, that he would be there.

"But let's jump back a little bit. Jack wanted to see you about something during the week. You yourself told me that. No, Jack didn't suspect you, but he thought that since you were connected with him through the school and the clinic, you might be able to keep tab on him.

"But the night of the party you saw the yearbooks Jack had collected and knew why he had them. And you were afraid that if he exposed Hal, the guy would think you had something to do with it and turn you in, too. So you came back. When your maid went back to sleep you simply detached the chime behind the door and left, being careful not to be seen. What did you do, swipe Jack's key to the place before you left? I don't doubt it. Then you got him in the bedroom. You shot him and watched him die. And while he tried to pull himself toward his gun you made a psychological study of a man facing death, telling the story, and drawing the chair back inch by inch until his body gave up. Then you went home. That was it, wasn't it? No, you don't have to answer me because there could be no other way."

(Now there were no more buttons. Slowly, ever so slowly, she pulled the blouse out of her skirt. It rustled faintly as silk does against wool. Then the cuff snaps—and she shrugged the blouse from her shoulders and let it fall to the floor. She wore no bra. Lovely shoulders. Soft curves of hidden muscles running across her body. Little ripples of excitement traversing the beautiful line of her neck. Breasts that were firm and inviting. Soft, yet so strong. She was so pretty. Young and delicious and exciting. She shook her head until her hair swirled in blond shimmering waves down her back.)

"But in the yearbooks you took from Jack's apartment were notations about Eileen. Her picture was in one, too, with Hal's. You knew that murder didn't stop there and saw how to cover one killing by committing another. You told Hal what you found, and sent him to threaten Eileen, and followed him in. Then, while the show went on, you killed them both, thinking that the murders would have to be hushed and the bodies disposed of by the others in the syndicate if they wanted to continue operation of the call house. You were right there. Somebody would have taken care of the matter if we hadn't come along so fast. When we crashed the joint you saw the madam run for it and followed her, and she never knew it, did she? How damn lucky you were. Coincidence and Lady Fortune were with you all the way. Neither Pat nor I thought to query *you* on an alibi for that night, but I bet you had a honey prepared.

"Let's not leave out George Kalecki. He found out about you. Hal must have gotten drunk and spilled the works. That's why he was surly the night of the party. He was worried and sore at Hal. Hal told you that George knew and you tried to pot him and missed. The only time you did miss. So he moved to town to get closer to the protection of the police. He couldn't tell them why, though, could he? You were still safe. He tried to implicate me to get me on the ball and run the killer down before the killer got to him.

"And after Hal's death, when we were walking along the park and George tried his hand with a gun, he wasn't shooting at me as I thought. It was you whom he wanted. He tailed me figuring I'd lead him to you. He knew he would be next on your list unless he got you first. George wanted out, but before he could blow he had to try to get the evidence Hal compiled or else take a chance on being sent to the chair if the stuff was ever found. Tough. I got him first. If he hadn't shot at me I wouldn't have killed him and he would have talked. I would have loved to make him yell his lungs out. Once more you were lucky."

(Her fingers were sliding the zipper of her skirt. The zipper and a button. Then the skirt fell in a heap around her legs. Before she stepped out of it she pushed the half slip down. Slowly, so I could get the entire exotic effect. Then together, she pushed them away with a toe. Long, graceful, tanned legs. Gorgeous legs. Legs that were all curves and strength and made me see pictures that I shouldn't see any more. Legs of a golden color that needed no stockings to enhance. Lovely legs that started from a flat stomach and rounded themselves into thighs that belonged more in the imagination than reality. Beautiful calves. Heavier than those you see in the movies. Passionate legs. All that was left were the transparent panties. And she was a real blonde.)

"Then Bobo Hopper. You didn't plan his death. It was an accident. Coincidence again that he had a former connection with George Kalecki. He had a job that he was proud of. He worked in your neighborhood running errands, delivering messages and sweeping floors. Only a simple moron who worked for nickels, but a happy egg. A guy that wouldn't step on ants and kept a bee-hive for a hobby. But one day he dropped a package he was de-livering for you—a prescription, you told him. He was afraid he'd lose his job, so he tried to get the prescription refilled at a drug-gist, and it turned out to be heroin that you were sending to a client. But meanwhile the client called you and said the messen-ger hadn't shown up. I was there in your apartment that day, re-member? And when I went for a haircut, you hurried out in your car, followed the route Bobo would have taken and saw him go in the drugstore, waited, and shot him when he came out.

"No, your alibi is shot. Kathy was home and never saw or heard you leave. You pretended to be in your darkroom, and no one ever disturbs a person in a darkroom. You detached the chimes and left, and came back without Kathy being any the wiser. But in your hurry you forgot to reconnect the chimes. I did it. Remember that, too? I came back for my wallet and there you were, a perfect alibi.

"Even then I didn't get it. But I started narrowing it down. I knew there was a motive that tied the thing up. Pat has a list of narcotic addicts. Someday, when they are cured, we'll get some-thing from them that will lay it at your feet.

"Myrna was next. Her death was another accident. You didn't plan this one, either, but it had to be. And when I left you at the tennis game it gave you the chance. When did the possibilities of the consequence of her leaving occur to you? Immediately, I bet, like Bobo. You have an incredible mind. Somehow you think of everything at once. You knew how Bobo's mind would work and what might have happened, and you knew the woman, too. That comes as a result of being a psychiatrist. I was asleep when you arrived at the Bellemy place. You had a coat the same color as Myrna's, but with a fur collar. And you knew, too, that women have a bad habit of trying on each other's clothes in private. You couldn't afford that chance because you had a deck of heroin in your coat pocket, or possibly traces of the stuff. And you were delivering it to Harmon Wilder and Charles Sherman—that's why they ran, because they had some of the junk on them.

"Yes, you were a little too late. Myrna found the stuff in your pocket. She knew what it was. She should. Until Jack came along she lived on the stuff. You found her with it in her hand and shot her. Then you took off your coat, threw it on the bed with the others, and put Myrna's on her while she lay there on the floor. As for powder burns, simple. Pull the nose out of a slug and fire the gun at her body as a blank. You even dropped the slug that went through her in the folds of the coat. Have you burned your coat yet? I bet—since it had powder burns on it. But some of the blue fibers were still under her fingernails, from a coat the same color as yours. That and the mirror was the final clue. That and the heroin you missed. A girl stands in front of a mirror for just one thing, especially in a room full of clothes.

"I don't know where you get your luck, Charlotte. You came in while the bartender went for a drink, but you couldn't afford to be seen going out. Not after you committed a murder. So you took the ledge around the building to the fire escape like a human fly. I was too broad to make it, but you weren't. You took your shoes off, didn't you? That's why there were no scratches in the cement. During the excitement of the game no one noticed you leave or return. Some kind of mass psychology, right?

"No, Charlotte, no jury would ever convict you on that, would they? Much too circumstantial. Your alibis were too perfect. You can't break an alibi that an innocent person believes is true. Like Kathy, for instance.

"But I would, Charlotte. And later we can take our time to worm out the truth without the interference of a court trial. We won't have to worry about a smart lawyer cracking our chains of circumstance and making them look foolish to a jury. We will know the answer as we do the problem, but the solution will take time. A trial wouldn't give us that time.

"No, Charlotte, I'm the jury now, and the judge, and I have a promise to keep. Beautiful as you are, as much as I almost loved you, I sentence you to death."

(Her thumbs hooked in the fragile silk of the panties and pulled them down. She stepped out of them as delicately as one coming from a bathtub. She was completely naked now. A suntanned goddess giving herself to her lover. With arms outstretched she walked toward me. Lightly, her tongue ran over her lips, making them glisten with passion. The smell of her was like an exhilarating perfume. Slowly, a sigh escaped her, making the hemispheres of her breasts quiver. She leaned forward to kiss me, her arms going out to encircle my neck.)

The roar of the .45 shook the room. Charlotte staggered back a step. Her eyes were a symphony of incredulity, an unbelieving witness to truth. Slowly, she looked down at the ugly swelling in her naked belly where the bullet went in. A thin trickle of blood welled out.

I stood up in front of her and shoved the gun into my pocket. I turned and looked at the rubber plant behind me. There on the table was the gun, with the safety catch off and the silencer still attached. Those loving arms would have reached it nicely. A face that was waiting to be kissed was really waiting to be splattered with blood when she blew my head off. My blood. When I heard her fall I turned around. Her eyes had pain in them now, the pain preceding death. Pain and unbelief.

"How c-could you?" she gasped.

I only had a moment before talking to a corpse, but I got it in. "It was easy," I said.

ABOUT THE AUTHOR

IN 1946, A young man wanted to build a house for his new bride. He purchased a plot of land in New York but lacked the additional one thousand dollars it would take to build the home. His solution: write a book. The result: *I, the Jury*, a blockbuster mystery that ultimately sold millions of copies. Mickey Spillane not only made the thousand dollars for his house (and then some) but went on to become one of the most successful mystery writers of the 20th century.

Frank Spillane was born on March 9, 1918, in Brooklyn, New York. He was baptized first in the Catholic Church (his father's religion) with the middle name Michael, and later in the Protestant Church (his mother's religion) with the middle name Morrison. While he was known as "Morrison" by his schoolteachers, he eventually went by "Mickey," the nickname his bartender father had always used. At school, the young Spillane excelled at sports, especially football and swimming. In high school he began to dabble in writing, and his first piece was published shortly after he graduated, under the pseudonym "Frank Morrison."

Following high school, Spillane enrolled in Fort Hayes State College in Kansas, though he played football more than he hit the books. College did not suit him, and he soon dropped out. Leaving Kansas, Spillane returned to New York, working briefly at Gimbel's department store. Bored, he decided to try comic book writing. He developed a comic book character called Mike Danger, who was a private detective. As his comic book career grew, Spillane's work appeared in publications such as *Captain America*, *Captain Marvel*, and *The Human Torch*.

World events soon interfered with Spillane's budding comic-book career, and he enlisted in the air force shortly after World War II broke out. There, he became a fighter pilot and was promoted to fighter pilot instructor, which kept him stateside rather than in the action overseas. The upside was that while stationed at Greenwood, Mississippi, he met his first wife, Mary Ann Pearce, and they married in 1945. Eventually they would have four children, Kathy, Ward, Michael, and Caroline.

When the war ended, Spillane moved his family to New York. Needing cash to build his first home, he set his sights on writing a crime novel. Basing his lead character on his comic book creation Mike Danger, Spillane dashed off *I, the Jury* in a matter of weeks. Thus, tough-guy private eye Mike Hammer was born, one of the most recognized—and notorious—names in crime fiction. Published in 1947, the hardcover edition sold somewhat poorly, but when the paperback version appeared, sales soared into the millions, and Spillane's new career was off and running.

I, the Jury became such a stunning success that Spillane quickly penned several more Mike Hammer novels, five of them published between 1950 and 1952. One, called *The Long Wait* (1952), sold three million copies in a single week. Each book sold over a million copies. However, while fans loved series character Mike

Hammer, a handful of the more staid critics were sometimes harsh on Hammer's vigilante-justice style, the very thing readers loved. While Mike Hammer's no-nonsense, tough-guy, womanizing character greatly appealed to the post–World War II servicemen audience Spillane was targeting, some critics did not understand or appreciate Hammer's rough edges. Spillane kept writing to his enormous fan base, which numbered in the multimillions, but privately he was hurt by the criticism.

Between 1952 and 1961, Spillane stopped writing full-length novels after becoming a Jehovah's Witness. He kept busy with a colorful array of unusual activities, from appearing in Miller Lite beer advertisements to joining a circus where he did trampoline acts and was shot out of a cannon. In addition, the adventurous author participated in stock-car racing, flying, fencing, diving for sunken treasure, and acting, including appearing as himself in *Ring of Fear*, a film produced by John Wayne.

After a decade of dabbling in other pursuits, Spillane returned to writing and penned *The Deep* (1961) and *The Girl Hunters* (1962), which featured the long-anticipated return of Mike Hammer. *The Girl Hunters* was made into a movie and starred none other than Spillane himself as Mike Hammer. He is the only mystery writer to portray his sleuth on film.

In 1965, he married for a second time, years after a divorce from Mary Ann. His new wife was Sherri (Selma) Malinou, an actress and model who appeared on the covers of several Mike Hammer/Mickey Spillane paperbacks. Much of their married life was spent apart, with Spillane living in Murrells Inlet, South Carolina, where he wrote and fished, and Selma pursuing her acting career in New York and Hollywood. The marriage ended in 1983.

A few years before the divorce, Spillane published his first young adult novel, *The Day the Sea Rolled Back* (1979), which won a Junior Literary Guild Award. He followed this up several years later with another youth novel, *The Ship that Never Was*.

In October 1983, Spillane married his third wife, Jane Johnson, a fitness instructor and former beauty queen who was 28 years his junior. During this time, Spillane was involved in the highly successful television series *Mike Hammer* (1984–1987), which starred Stacy Keach as the hard-hitting detective.

In 1995, Mickey Spillane received the Grand Master award from the Mystery Writers of America. The legendary creator of the legendary Mike Hammer remains one of the top-selling authors of all time, with impressive overall sales of more than 130 million books.

Spillane always recognized that he was a reader's writer, not a snobby literary author. "Those big shot writers could never dig the fact that there are more salted peanuts consumed than caviar," he said. He also believed that "if the public likes you, you're good." And clearly, the public loves Spillane.